The Voice Inside
A practical guide for and about people who hear voices

Written and edited by PAUL BAKER
with contributions from
MARIUS ROMME, SANDRA ESCHER
and RON COLEMAN

P&P
PRESS LTD

Published by P & P Press
28 Habost, Port of Ness, Isle of Lewis, HS2 0TG,
Tel: +44 (0)1851 810060
Email: info@workingtorecovery.co.uk
www.workingtorecovery.co.uk

ISBN: 978-0-956304-81-0

*This book is dedicated to the memory of
Hannelore Kafke, John Williams, Terence McLaughlin
and Micky Devaldo – who were members of the
international hearing voices movement*

Did You Know?

- Studies have found that between four and 10 per cent of people across the world hear voices.
- Between 70 and 90 cent of people who hear voices do so following traumatic events.
- Voices can be male, female, without gender, child, adult, human or non-human.
- People may hear one voice or many. Some people report hearing hundreds, although in almost all reported cases, one dominates above the others.
- Voices can be experienced in the head, in the ears, outside the head, in some other part of the body, or in the environment.
- Voices often reflect important aspects of the hearer's emotional state – emotions that are often unexpressed by the hearer.

"What this research shows is that we must accept that the voices exist. We must also accept that we cannot change the voices. They are not curable, just as you cannot cure left-handedness – human variations are not open to cure – only to coping. Therefore to assist people to cope we should not give them therapy that does not work. We should let people decide for themselves what helps or not. It takes time for people to accept that hearing voices is something that belongs to them."

Marius Romme

Contents

FOREWORD   IX
ABOUT THE AUTHOR   XI
ACKNOWLEDGEMENTS   XIII
WHY WE HAVE WRITTEN THIS GUIDE   XV

TWELVE ESSENTIAL FACTS ABOUT THE EXPERIENCE
OF HEARING VOICES   3

INTRODUCTION   7
  A fresh approach   7
  A chance meeting   9
  Why I got involved   10
  Recovery   14
  Breaking the rules   17

PART 1: THE HEARING VOICES MOVEMENT   19
  The importance of listening   22
  Why "Hearing Voices"   27
  Professor Marius Romme gets a shock and
  founds a movement   28
  How did it start in the UK?   31
  What is the significance of the hearing voices
  moment for voice hearers?   33

PART 2: PEOPLE WHO HEAR VOICES   37
  Hearing voices in history and religion   38
  What do the voices tell you and what   45
  can they do?   45
  Voices and their relationship with the voice hearer   47

Exploring the meaning of voices   48
Voices are heard by "normal people" and can be
sometimes be a positive experience   51
Children and Young People who Hear Voices   56

PART 3: WHAT TO DO ABOUT VOICES THAT
CAUSE YOU PROBLEMS   59
How to zap voices you don't like   63
Making Sense of voices   69

PART 4: HELPING PEOPLE WHO HEAR VOICES
THAT CAUSE PROBLEMS   74
What Marius Romme says   74
Hearing voices: Don't kill the messenger   75
Implications for Friends and relatives and people
who hear voices   77
hears voices: 78
Implications for mental health workers   79
what they do   82
Talking to and with Challenging Voices   88
voice hearers?   90

PART 5: THE FUTURE?   93
Hearing voices and the implications for
schizophrenia   93
What Next?   100

GLOSSARY OF TERMS COMMONLY USED IN PSYCHIATRY AND
PSYCHIATRIC RESEARCH   107
FURTHER READING   112

TABLES

TABLE I: THE CORE CONCEPTS INFORMING OUR WORK
ON HEARING VOICES   1

TABLE II: VOICE HEARING QUESTIONNAIRE   24

TABLE III: FAMOUS PEOPLE WHO HEARD VOICES   37

TABLE IV: WHAT DOES IT FEEL LIKE TO HEAR VOICES?   42

TABLE V: HEARING VOICES AMONGST "NORMAL PEOPLE"   50

TABLE VI: WHAT YOU CAN DO IF YOUR CHILD TELLS YOU
THEY ARE HEARING VOICES: A 10-POINT CHECK-LIST   57

TABLE VII: THREE PHASES FOUND AMONG PEOPLE
WHO HEAR VOICES   60

TABLE VIII: STRATEGIES FOR COPING WITH
DISTRESSING VOICES   64

TABLE IX: WHY HEARING VOICES IN ITSELF IS NOT A
SYMPTOM OF ILLNESS   73

TABLE X: AN EXERCISE IN HOW TO REPLICATE THE
EXPERIENCE OF HEARING VOICES   76

TABLE XI: TALK ABOUT IT: A HEARING VOICES CHECKLIST 85

TABLE XII: NEW DIALOGUES ON VOICES   91

TABLE XIII: THE PROBLEM WITH SCHIZOPHRENIA   95

FOREWORD

This handbook is an updated and combined version of two previously published booklets I wrote over ten years ago introducing the subject of hearing voices, they were called *Can You Hear Me* and *The Voice Inside*.

The Voice Inside was first published in 1996, as an introduction to the research and practical work on hearing voices and written for people who hear voices and their family and friends. Since then the booklet has been reprinted many times and has sold thousands of copies and has been translated into German, French, Polish, Spanish, Norwegian, Polish, Swedish, whilst on-line versions can be found on the Mind[1], Mental Health Foundation[2] and INTERVOICE[3] websites.

A second booklet, *Can you Hear Me* was also published in 1996. It aimed to assist mental health workers by providing information on ways that people with overpowering voices could be helped to cope with their experiences. This booklet has been in print ever since and is currently published by P&P Press[4].

I was persuaded by my friend Ron Coleman, who published the first two books, that it was about time to write a second edition. I agreed (eventually) and we decided it would be a good idea to combine and revise the two booklets and

---

1. Mind (UK) www.mind.org.uk/Information/Booklets/Other/The+voice+inside.htm

2. Mental Health Foundation (UK) www.mentalhealth.org.uk/information/mental-health-a-z/hearing-voices/

3. INTERVOICE www.intervoiceonline.org

4. P&P Press http://www.workingtorecovery.co.uk

bring them up to date by including the exciting developments that have taken place since the guides were first published.

This much expanded introduction and practical guide to voices is the result.

Inside you will find lots of new information about the experience of hearing voices; with advice about how to cope and make sense of the experience and descriptions for voice hearers and workers of new ways of helping to cope better with troubling voices.

Paul Baker

ABOUT THE AUTHOR

Paul Baker is a community development and group worker. Paul has worked in the health care and education sectors for the last 30 years. He has helped to develop innovative mental health care services in the community including services run by the people who use them, self-advocacy services, supported housing services, social firms and enterprises as well as the development of forums for people to enable them to have a direct input in the development and running of services. For fifteen years Paul was the chairperson of a large housing association for homeless people in Manchester.

Paul was one of the founding members of the Hearing Voices Network in England and is currently the coordinator of INTERVOICE, the influential coordinating body for the international hearing voices movement. He also specialises in assisting organisations in harnessing and developing on-line communities to complement and support their work. More recently Paul has worked with the Mental Health Foundation, Working to Recovery, Radish Online Ltd and the Scottish Hearing Voices Network.

He has a special interest in working with groups of people to find ways to help themselves overcome difficulties and problems. He also has a strong commitment to forging international partnerships in the development and sharing of progressive and effective mental health services.

Paul has published books and written chapters and articles for many publications on mental health issues. He provides consultancy services, lectures and trains on empowerment and recovery issues and the relationships these have to effective mental health service delivery.

If you chase away my devils, my angels may leave too.

Tom Waits

ACKNOWLEDGEMENTS

There are many people I would like to thank:

Firstly, I want to express my gratitude to Professor Marius Romme[5] and Sandra Escher for their inspiration and support and especially for the information that can be found in the key books, *Accepting Voices* (1993) and *Making Sense of Voices* (2000) published by MIND and the many other books they have contributed to and articles they have written over the years.

I want to acknowledge those voice hearers who have sought to find new ways of thinking about the problems they have and have found constructive solutions both inside and outside of the world of psychiatry. I particularly want to thank all those members of the international fellowship of voice hearers and their allies. They have striven to redefine the so-called symptoms of the "disease" called schizophrenia as understandable personal experiences, which although sometimes distressing, can certainly be overcome. They have inspired this book.

Thanks also to those researchers and workers and others throughout the world who have worked so hard to promote

---

5. Marius Anton Joannes Romme (born 17 January 1934, Amsterdam) is a Dutch psychiatrist. He is best known for his work on hearing voices (auditory hallucinations) and regarded as the founder and principle theorist for the Hearing Voices Movement. From 1974 to 1999 he was professor of social psychiatry at the Medical Faculty of the University of Maastricht (Netherlands), as well as consultant psychiatrist at the Community Mental Health Centre in Maastricht. He is now visiting professor at the Mental Health Policy Centre, University of Central England in Birmingham.

this new way of thinking about hearing voices. It is their ideas, speeches and writings that have had an important influence on this publication.

Lastly (but by no means least) I would like to thank Ron Coleman and Karen Taylor for their energetic and sympathetic role in ensuring this book came to print.

WHY WE HAVE WRITTEN THIS GUIDE

This guide has been written for voice hearers, family and friends, as well as being of interest to professionals working with voice hearers. It has been written on behalf of the Hearing Voices Movement[6] as an introduction to the different way of thinking about "hearing voices". Much of the information in this book is taken from the work of voice hearers and mental health workers and researchers from around the world, including the pioneering work of the psychiatrist Professor Marius Romme, Dr Sandra Escher, Ron Coleman and many others. We have written it to:

Fill an information gap

To date, not so much has been written about this experience and its meaning that is aimed at people who hear voices. Why is this? Well, for a long time hearing voices has been regarded as just another symptom of a mental illness, therefore meaningless and unworthy of further discussion (and this is still the case is in some parts of the world) – and secondly – unsurprisingly given the way voices are regarded, it is considered a socially stigmatising experience that most people have kept to themselves. This remains the prevailing view particularly in the USA and many parts of the western world. We hope this guide will help to change this situation.

---

6. You can read a full account of the development and impact of the Hearing Voices Movement at Wikipedia http://en.wikipedia.org/wiki/Hearing_Voices_Movement

To break the silence and lift the lid by asking people who hear voices what is going on for them

The lack of information available to voice hearers about what their experiences may mean, has in some cases, been made worse by the approach taken by psychiatry. As I said above, and it's worth repeating, for many years psychiatry has regarded voices as something it calls "auditory hallucinations" and a symptom of conditions such as schizophrenia, manic depression and other mental illnesses. Because psychiatry thought the voices were a symptom of an illness, they saw little point in investigating the meaning of the hearing voices experience, or indeed even asking voice hearers what was happening for them. Talking about voices with a voice hearer was regarded as a dangerous thing to do as this could be considered as buying into the delusional world of an ill person.

Further, psychiatrists, nurses and other professionals have been taught that there is not a lot an individual can do for themselves to cope with the voices. Indeed, professionals are often taught not to engage voice hearers about the content of their voice experience and instead sought to distract the voice hearer from their voices and if necessary to administer medication (major tranquillisers) to reduce these delusions and hallucinations. However, as readers may be aware not everyone responds to this type of treatment and continue to hear voices (about 30%), even those voice hearers who do stop hearing voices experience unpleasant unwanted side effects from the medication.

However, we found out that not asking people who heard voices about their experiences was mistaken, in fact critical information that could help people to recover had been neglected for years because of the view held by psychiatry that voices were meaningless.

We also discovered two very important things about voices, simply by asking people who hear voices about their experience – something that had not really been done before in a systematic way[7].

Firstly, our surveys revealed that whilst hearing voices could sometimes be a disturbing experience and lead to becoming a patient, there were many people who heard voices and coped well with their voices, doing so without psychiatric intervention.

Secondly, we made a further quite astonishing discovery that was equally important and at the time mostly unknown – our research showed that there are many people who hear voices who can cope with their voices and regard them as a positive part of their lives.

To share what we had learnt

What our research and work has shown is that hearing voices is not always a negative experience or even if it is negative for you, it doesn't have to stay that way. Neither has it always been regarded as a negative experience, the idea that voices is part of an illness is not correct – throughout history and today there are people who hear voices who find their voices inspirational and comforting.

These are facts that on the face of it are hard to square with the extremely negative way that the experience is regarded by psychiatry. For this reason researchers, practitioners and

---

7. Voice Hearing – A Questionnaire, Developed by Sandra Escher, Patsy Hage and Marius Romme with revisions by Monique Pennings

voice hearers have come together to form the Hearing Voices Movement[8] to challenge the view that voice hearing is part of a psychiatric disease syndrome and needs to be eradicated. Rather, we consider it to be more akin to a variation in human experience – if you like, a faculty or differentiation – something like left handedness or homosexuality, that it is definitely not open to cure.

We want you to read on

The information in this guide is based on research and practical work carried out in 19 countries over the last seventeen years, which for the first time comes directly from the real experts, the voice hearers themselves. In this guide we seek to answer three fundamental questions:

what is it like to hear voices?
why does it start and what does it mean?
and how can people cope better – and – be helped to
    cope with this experience if it is troubling them?

We hope that when you read the guide you will be interested in finding out more. If you would like to, you can join INTERVOICE: International Hearing Voices Network and keep in touch with developments as well as supporting their work. Email admin@intervoiceonline.org

---

8. Hearing Voices Movement, information from Wikipedia, the free encyclopaediaa, http://en.wikipedia.org/wiki/Hearing_Voices_Movement

Table I: The core concepts informing our work on hearing voices:

Our research and work has shown:

• Hearing voice is in itself not a sign of mental illness
• Hearing voices are experienced by a great many people, who do so without becoming ill.
• Hearing voices is often related to problems in the life history of the voice hearer.
• To recover from the distress the person who hears voices has to learn to cope with their voice and the original problems that lay at their roots of their voice hearing experience

TWELVE ESSENTIAL FACTS ABOUT THE EXPERIENCE OF HEARING VOICES

1. Voice hearing is often seen as a prime symptom of psychosis[9]. Hearing voices (aka auditory hallucinations) is also considered a first rank symptom of schizophrenia[10]. There are three main psychiatric categories of patients that hear voices;

- schizophrenia (around 50%);
- affective psychosis (around 25%)
- dissociative disorders (around 80%)

2. However, hearing voices in itself is not a symptom of an illness, but is apparent in 2–4 % of the population, some research gives higher estimates and even more people (about 8%) have so called "peculiar personal convictions", that are sometimes called "delusions", and do so without being ill. Many people who hear voices find them helpful or benevolent[11]. In a large study of 15,000 people in the USA it was found that there was a prevalence of 2.3% who had heard voices frequently and this contrasts with the 1% prevalence of schizophrenia.

3. Whilst one in three people who hear voices will become a psychiatric patient – two in three people can cope well and

9. American Psychiatric Association 1994

10. K Schneider, MW Hamilton, *Clinical Psychopathology* (1959) Grune & Stratton

11. Romme M and Escher S: (Eds.), *Accepting Voices* (1993, second edition 1998), 258 pages, Mind Publications, London

are in no need of psychiatric care. No diagnosis can be given because these two out of three people who hear voices are quite healthy and function well. It is very significant that in our society there are more people who hear voices who have never been psychiatric patients than there are people who hear voices and become psychiatric patients.

4. Brain imaging has confirmed that voice hearers do experience a sound as if there were a real person talking to them[12].

5. A study by Honig[13] and other researchers from Maastricht examined the differences between non-patient and patients hearing voices, it was found to be not in the form of the voices but the content. In other words the non-patients heard voices both inside and outside their head as did the patients but either the content was positive or the hearer had a positive view of the voice and felt in control of it. By contrast the patient group were more frightened of the voices and the voices were more critical and malevolent and they felt less control over them.

6. Psychiatry in our western culture often unjustly identifies hearing voices with schizophrenia. Going to a psychiatrist with hearing voices gives you an 80% chance of getting a

12. SS Shergill, MJ Brammer, SCR Williams, RM Murray, (2000) *Mapping auditory hallucinations in schizophrenia using functional magnetic resonance imaging,* Archives of General Psychiatry, 2000

13. Honig, A.; Romme. M.; Ensink, B.; Escher, S.; Pennings, M.; Devries, M.W. (1998): *Auditory Hallucinations: A Comparison between Patients and Non patients.* The Journal of Nervous and Mental Disease, 186 (10), 646-651

diagnosis of schizophrenia[14].

7. Conventional approaches in psychiatry to the problem of voice hearing have been to ignore the meaning of the experience for the voice hearer and concentrate on removing the symptoms (auditory hallucinations) by the use of physical means such as medication[15]. Although anti psychotic medication is helpful to some sufferers of psychosis[16], there are a significant proportion of patients (30 per cent) that still experience the 'symptoms' such as hearing voices despite very high doses of injected anti psychotic.

8. Further anti-psychotic medication prevents the emotional processing and therefore healing, of the meaning of the voices[17].

9. Traditional practice in behavioural psychology concentrated on either distracting the patient or ignoring references by the patient to the voice hearing experience, with the hope that the patient would concentrate on 'real' experiences, which would then be positively reinforced (the assumption being that the voice hearing was a delusional belief). The effect of this approach is to discourage the discussion about the voice hearing experience but without eradicating it[18].

---

14. Romme & Escher 2001

15. Romme & Escher, 1989

16. WW Fleischhacker, *Pharmacological treatment of schizophrenia: a review,* Schizophrenia, 2002

17. Romme & Escher, 2000

18. P.D.J. Chadwick, Birchwood, & Trower, 1996

10. In research concerning people who hear voices it was found that 77% of the people diagnosed with schizophrenia the hearing of voices was related to traumatic experiences. These traumatic experiences varied from being sexually abused, physically abused, being extremely belittled over long periods from young age, being neglected during long periods as a youngster, being very aggressively treated in marriage, not being able to accept ones sexual identity and other circumstances that people found difficult[19].

11. Hearing voices in itself is not related to the illness of schizophrenia. In population research (that is large scale research studies involving thousands of people) only 16% of the whole group of voice hearers can be diagnosed with schizophrenia[20].

12. The prognosis (will you get better or not) of hearing voices is more positive than generally is perceived. In Sandra Escher's research with children hearing voices she followed 82 children over a period of four years. In that period 64% of the children's voices disappeared congruently with learning to cope with emotions and becoming less stressed. In children with whom the voices were psychiatrised and made a part of an illness and not given proper attention, voices did not vanish, but became worse, the development of those children was delayed[21].

---

19. Romme & Escher 2006
20. Romme & Escher 2001
21. Romme & Escher 2006

INTRODUCTION

A fresh approach

As you will know by now, to hear a voice that has no apparent physical cause is usually regarded by psychiatry as an auditory hallucination, a sign of a mental illness. It is most often regarded as an important symptom of schizophrenia (although voices can also occur in manic depressive and dissociative disorders) and no doubt many of you reading this book, will be doing so, because of your concerns about this illness, perhaps you have been diagnosed as having schizophrenia yourself or know someone who has. It is possible that the hearing of voices (as we prefer to call them or auditory hallucinations as psychiatrists call them) are an important part of the distress that the illness causes you. It is also possible that other readers of this book hear voices and are troubled by them, but so far have not sought medical assistance and may not have done so because the popular perception of hearing voices is very negative. We all know and probably fear the stereotyped voice hearers' we sometimes see walking in the street conducting an animated conversation with themselves.

There is a well worn joke about talking to yourself being the first sign of a nervous breakdown and it is certainly a behaviour that is likely to have the label of "mad" stamped on it, and no one really likes to think of themselves as mad. A third group of readers might also hear voices and wonder what all the fuss is about, they might be quite comfortable with the experience and don't think it is a problem at all, although understandably, are deterred from talking to other

7

people about it because of what they might think of them if they did say anything. Unsurprisingly then, hearing voices is not generally talked about because it is thought of as a socially stigmatising and unwanted experience.

Because of these prevailing attitudes, it is most important that I point out, right at the beginning of this book, that this has by no means always been the case, and one of the main reasons that this book has been written is to show that there are many people who hear voices who can cope with their voices and regard them as a positive part of their lives. Neither is it the case that voices have always been regarded as a negative experience – throughout history and even today there are people who hear voices who find their voices inspirational and comforting. These are facts, that on the face of it are hard to square with the extremely negative way that the experience is regarded by psychiatry. This is in no way an attempt to deny or belittle the very disturbing effect voices can have, both for the person who hears voices, and their family and friends. The voices can be hostile, controlling and seek to undermine the voice hearer's own self-esteem. Many people feel overwhelmed by the consequences of this experience and end up seeking medical assistance. It often seems as if there is little that the people themselves and the people around them can do to regain control of their lives and that was certainly my initial experience. The sense of powerlessness that this can bring seems to be an almost inevitable feature of the experience and is reinforced by the fact that most medical advice presumes that the person suffering from the experience of hearing voices is a passive victim of the experience and generally avoids talking about voices at all. We do not think this has to be the case and in this book we hope that we will show that voice hearers and those around them can do to a lot to help themselves to improve their control over the voices.

A *chance meeting*

This work began for me with one of those strange coincidences that change the course of your life.

In 1988 I met two remarkable people, Marius Romme and Sandra Escher in Italy at a World Health Organisation sponsored conference entitled "The Question of Psychiatry". Marius, a professor of psychiatry and his colleague, Sandra, a science journalist, were presenting information and results about their work on "hearing voices" which they had begun two years earlier. Hearing voices was a subject that I knew something about, but like most people working in mental health, I was very confused about what I thought about this puzzling and sometimes frightening experience. However, during the conference they discussed their work with me and it was not long before I was hooked, both by the approach they had adopted and the way that they had got involved in the subject. At the time, the early results of their research were leading to some startling conclusions, many of which where at odds with the orthodox psychiatric opinion I have described above. As a result when they started publishing their findings and talking about them to other professionals they were subject, unsurprisingly perhaps, to a lot of suspicion and even ridiculed. Some psychiatrists were wondering if Marius was himself hearing voices. As a consequence of this initial feedback Marius and Sandra had made a priority of searching for allies, people who might be prepared to carry out similar investigations in their own countries.

Apparently, for some reason they thought I fitted the

bill and asked me to come to Maastricht to see what they were doing and to attend a conference they were holding, I could hardly say no and a few weeks later I found myself in Holland and at the beginning of ten years of intriguing and challenging work. I have to admit, that almost from the start, I was an enthusiastic supporter of their work and what they were trying to achieve. This was partly because my brother experienced an intense form of voice hearing which eventually led to him being hospitalised by a psychiatrist for a short time (see below) In fact it was his experience that gave me the conviction that another more constructive way of helping people who heard voices had to be found. I suppose because Marius and Sandra thought that voices were actually perceived by "hearers" and that these voices had meaning beyond being merely hallucinations was the main reason I had confidence in the seemingly unconventional idea that voices could be real.

Why I got involved

Over twenty five years ago my brother experienced what he thought of as a spiritual awakening, at times troubling, even frightening and at other times enjoyable and enlightening. Talking about this later, he said he felt he needed to embrace this new world he was living within. This experience occurred shortly after he had moved to live in Manchester following the break up of a long term relationship and resigning a job in advertising.

At this time I thought I knew a lot about mental health issues and had become, what you could call a mental health activist, campaigning for better services for people with mental illnesses. I had seen for myself the negative aspects of psychiatry such as the over use of anti psychotic medication; the unnecessary use of electro convulsive therapy (ECT) and its lack of interest in developing support services in the community. As a member of a local association of Mind (the mental health charity) I was part of an attempt to change the nature and role of mental health services. An initiative that emphasised the importance of working alongside people with mental health problems, rather than for them. This led to the development of; self-help groups drop in centres and employment projects amongst others, all aimed at trying to destigmatise mental illness and provide routes back into society. None of this helped though when my brother began to behave and think very differently than he usually did. In spite of my best efforts to keep him out of psychiatry, which by now I had little faith in, he ended up in a hospital and was diagnosed as schizophrenic. The happy ending to this story is that his time in hospital was short. My brother is living an "ordinary" life, teaches tai chi and is a father.

In a way, my lack of faith in his theory of what was happening to him was a kind of betrayal. I was the same as most other professionals – I was so blinded by the supposed scientific credibility of schizophrenia that I was unable to fully accept an alternative explanation. Rather, I rationalised Alan's experience as a case of non-recurring schizophrenia (this is said to happen) or that he was given the wrong diagnosis. Later, it began to occur to me that what he said was right and what I thought was wrong. Although my doubts about the meaning began to form, I had a problem working out what I could do about it. During this time I felt useless and even sometimes part of the problem as I tried to understand what my brother was going through. But, all I had to offer, really, were some professional platitudes about not listening to what the voices said. This was an extremely limited approach that really only amounted to trying to distract him from this internal voice experience, which obviously meant a lot to him, but from which I felt excluded from and threatened by.

The experience he was having was obviously very profound and meaningful to him, he seemed to me to be really alive and in touch with his experiences, he was articulate about what was happening to him, although for me it remained a mysterious and strangely mystical experience. I could not understand how he had transformed into a person I sometimes did not know. Although I could see that there was joy in what he experienced, there was also pain and bewilderment (including to the reactions of the people around him) and a vulnerability due to his total commitment to really experiencing what was happening to him. Unsurprisingly, my attempts to help him were hindered by my own anxieties and fears. It became obvious, that even though I was a mental health worker, there was little I could do to prevent him from being hospitalised and subjected to a form of treatment I had little faith in and had seen fail for many other people. Even though I had always been concerned to promote and support forms of work that assisted people in maintaining their own autonomy in the face of what sometimes could be very distressing symptoms, I found myself helpless in the face of my brothers experience. Not much use to him at all, as it happened.

There was a sort of happy ending to this tale as he quickly found his own route out of traditional treatment and he lived for a time in a therapeutic community run by an organisation called the Philadelphia Association where close friends of ours worked. Although it took him some time, he found his own explanations and ways of coping with his voices, outside of psychiatry. His main regret being that there was no one to provide the kind of support that he needed to understand the crisis he was in. This is what he wrote about what such support might look like:

The experience for a "psychotic" is an overwhelming one. It's like being thrown into a turbulent river of change and not being able to swim or being in an alien world without a guidebook and unable to read the signposts. I suggest that we need to learn to swim or that we are taught the language and know a little about this world before we get there. Obviously the confusion and fear associated with an unexpected arrival would result in distress and often an inability to function. This is added to by the social/cultural response to the individuals apparent loss of control.

I would like to make the proposition that the so-called psychotic state is an involuntary and unexpected immersion into the world of the subconscious. I use the term subconscious warily but find it a useful means of labelling a part of human consciousness that allows for experience that has been described by so many different people in so many different ways i.e. the psychotic, the shaman, the mystic, the visionary and so on.

The view that the psychotic is accessing the subconscious and experiencing phenomena shared by these other groups is not readily accepted, however neither is the view that these other groups are also experiencing the same thing. To put it crudely it is a case of 'my' God versus 'your' God.

I hope one day those who may experience a so called psychosis in the future and mostly those that already do so will be able to find this kind of support. I would hope that this would empower individuals by putting their experience

13

on a more positive footing and by putting the experience into a framework and context that can be easily related to. In addition I would hope that once so empowered the individual might be enabled to seek out or take up an established practice and transform an otherwise negative experience into a positive one.

My brother's experience, although troubling and at times scary (whilst at other times funny and enlightening) had shown me something of great significance, that the psychosis or immersion, was for my brother an experience that had meaning and significance for him. It was also something that he was able to work through for himself and crucially could and did have a positive outcome. This is not supposed to be possible, psychiatry regards such experiences as symptoms of psychotic illnesses and requiring treatment, something my brother avoided as he did the label of being a schizophrenic. He recovered (a possibility that psychiatry also regards with scepticism, they would rather use the term in remission) and did so without the assistance of psychiatric intervention, except for the brief stay at the beginning of the experience, without medication and without losing his autonomy. I didn't understand how this could be, but I did know that at the time, in spite of my own criticisms of psychiatry, I had no other way of regarding his experience except as being that of a mental illness.

Recovery

In the early 1990s I met Ron Coleman, who had by then spent ten years in and out of the psychiatric system and was diagnosed as having a particularly severe form of schizophrenia. When I first met Ron he was unshaven, unkempt and unwashed. He seemed from the outside to be barely functioning at all, his eyes were like that of a sleeping person forced to hold their eyes open and somehow staying asleep at the same time. He had more rings under his eyes than an ancient tree and the pallor of someone unused to daylight. His aspect was tragic and he emanated pain. This guy was on very high-level anti-psychotic medication and still suffering from some kind of extreme inner torment. What it was though I wasn't going to find out for some time, as Ron said nothing to anyone. I knew Ron because he used to attend the hearing voices self help group held in Manchester, he came with his support worker and to be honest, besides thinking he was probably the illest-looking person I'd seen outside of a hospital I didn't have much to do with him. Of course when I say he looked ill, it was physically ill, not mentally ill (how do you look mentally ill) and there was a good reason for this, besides physical neglect, it was also the impact of high doses of neuroleptics. Ron came to the self-help groups for some time and although saying little he became friends with Mike Grierson and Terry McLaughlin, members of the Manchester Hearing Voices Network.

In spite of all the odds seeming to be stacked up against him, he still managed to make a full recovery. By a full recovery, I mean that Ron, who had for many years experienced severe emotional distress – which prevented him from working and even sometimes from functioning at all – managed to pick up his life again. This was a process that was to transform Ron's life, from being a 'victim', constantly hospitalised, heavily medicated, living a life that was fragmented by the disruption his illness caused him – he became 'victor' and found a way of harnessing the people around him, to such a constructive effect, that from the point of making the decision that he wanted to recover, to the point where Ron could say he was recovered took a surprisingly short period of time.

Ultimately, Ron completely gave up his psychiatric status; this is something that is now in the past. This was by no means an easy journey but it was a worthwhile one. Now, Ron does not regard himself as having a mental illness, he no longer takes medication or receives any other form of treatment. Although Ron still hears voices, he no longer even has the other "symptoms" that led him to seek assistance in the first place. What this experience did leave though, was a scar, that needs to heal, the recognition that perhaps the ten years in and out of psychiatric care need not have happened at all?

As somebody who had the privilege to be part of Ron's life at this time, the two things that struck me about this whole experience were, firstly, after making the decision that he was going to work toward recovery, Ron always refused to give in and secondly he always asked those people around him to be a part of the process of his recovery. In a way we all recovered together, this was not only Ron's success story; it also restored the confidence and self-belief of the workers and friends who took part in the recovery. He asked for our best and he gave us his. What I've taken from this is that recovery in many ways is both an individual and collective experience. We are all recovering to one degree or another.

When this recovery occurred it seemed to be such an unusual event that professional mental health workers and fellow users of mental health services did not know how to react. They were frankly, suspicious and doubting, either believing that he was wrongly diagnosed or would soon become ill again. To recover from your illness, became for some people rather a threatening development. Ron was

16

strongly affected both by the loss of ten years of his life as well as by the ambivalent response to his recovery. So, he has given much thought to what it was that really happened to enable his recovery. In a way it was this experience that made me look at the lessons that have been learnt about the recovery process. We have turned these into a practical guide, so that any one who wants to take this journey can benefit from Ron's experience and the many other people we have talked to about their own recoveries.

Breaking the rules

The information in this book is mainly drawn from the work of my friends and colleagues and other important contributors to the on-going debate that is taking place, right now, on the margins of the world of psychiatry – and – that I have had the good fortune to come across during the writing of this book. They are the experts, (either through personal experience or because they work with people with mental health problems) who although regarded as dissidents within psychiatry, have spoken and written about the limitations of psychiatry with refreshing candour.

More importantly they share in common the determination to break one of the unwritten rules of the professional game; by regarding each other as equals, allies and human beings. It is these people who continue to attempt to provoke positive changes in psychiatry, so it can at last play a constructive role in resolving the problems faced by our fellow citizens. This book is based on the lessons they have learnt and is intended as a tribute to their struggle to defeat the scientific monolith that is schizophrenia and replace it with a theory of mental health problems and psychiatric practice, that is both more humane and more effective.

In writing this book every effort has been made to make it readable and wherever possible I have tried to avoid unnecessary technical and scientific terms, or where they are required, to ensure that the terms are explained. For this reason there is a glossary at the end of the book. I have written it in this way because much of the source material for this book is written in technical language. In my view this is a pity because it has served to hide the fact from voice hearers that some very significant work is being carried out into the experience of voice hearing, especially as it relates both to normality and to so-called mental illness.

PART 1: THE HEARING VOICES MOVEMENT

In November 1988 I was invited by Professor Romme to attend a conference in Maastricht entitled "People Who Hear Voices". The conference was held in the MECC, a prestigious National Conference Centre in Maastricht, Netherlands, and was organised jointly, by Resonance (a self help organisation of people who hear voices) and the Department of Social Psychiatry at Limburg University. The conference was an opportunity for professionals to hear the direct experiences of people who hear voices, alongside current theoretical frameworks as to what the phenomenon means. It also presented a radical explanation as to the meaning of hearing voices for individuals, and ways that people could cope with this experience.

The key to this explanation was to take hearing voices out of the sickness model and such was the credibility of this approach in Holland, that the meeting was opened by the Chief Inspector for Mental Health from the Ministry of Health & Welfare for the Netherlands. The conference followed three years of work, which presented many challenges to current understanding of hearing voices.

When I interviewed Marius Romme just after the conference he recalled that:

"Deciding to hold a conference was not my decision, but was the decision of the Foundation Resonance. The patients felt that professionals were not accepting the voices as reality. This time a smaller number of people hearing voices, and a larger number of professional people were invited. By talking and explaining their experiences to the professionals, they hoped to help enlighten people to what was actually

happening, as opposed to the professionals' theory of what was happening. They were trying to bridge the gap by enabling the professionals to meet normal, healthy people who heard voices without being psychotic. These people had learnt to cope with the voices by having their own theory which acted as an anchor for them."

This was the time I also met Patsy Hage, a young woman who was a patient of Marius who heard voices. It was Patsy who started the whole investigation into the meaning of voices in the Netherlands. Patsy's story is a fascinating and painful one, she was hearing destructive and negative voices that gave her orders, or forbade her to do things. When I met her, she told me that there were times when they could dominate her completely. Patsy, who was 30 years old at the time, had already been hospitalised several times and was diagnosed as suffering from a schizophrenic psychosis. She was given major tranquillisers (sometimes called neuroleptics or antipsychotics) like many other patients who hear voices, but they had no effect on neutralising or reducing the number or the insistance of the voices she heard, as the medication is meant to do. They did, however, reduce the anxiety she felt about the existence and nature of the voices, but at the same time they also lowered her mental alertness. Patsy, understandably, found this very disturbing and was depressed by her inability to feel and think like she used to be able to. It was during this time that Patsy began to talk about suicide more often, and her psychiatrist, Marius, felt that he might be unable to prevent her from taking a path of no return. Except for one positive element in their relationship, this could have been a sad but familiar story and which has led to the death of many people diagnosed as having schizophrenia.

The positive element was that Patsy had developed her own theory about her experience of hearing voices, as many other voice hearers have and that she had the good fortune to meet a psychiatrist who was prepared to take her seriously. As Patsy explained to Marius, it was her opinion that the voices were not part of an illness neither were they hallucinations, for they had been with her since she was eight years old, appearing shortly after she had been badly burnt (subsequently it has been shown that up to 70% of voice hearers first hear voices after a major trauma). At first the voices were friendly and helpful and for a long time they caused her no problems and it was only when she was fifteen years old that the voices became unfriendly and angry. Instead, Patsy explained that for her, the voices were real, part of who she was and although she now suffered as a result of what the voices told her, they still had meaning to her.

As Patsy said to Marius; "You believe in a God we never see or hear, so why shouldn't you believe in the voices I really do hear?" Marius was very impressed by Patsy's point of view, for like many other psychiatrists he had always dismissed voices as being part of the delusional and hallucinatory world of the psychiatrically ill. But there was something compelling about what she had said that made sense to Marius because it was certainly the case in our society that to believe in the existence of God, in spite of the lack of any physical evidence, is acceptable and no one who believes in this is thought of as mad, yet the same acceptance is not extended to those who psychiatry regards as hallucinators. After struggling to accept this rather startling point of view for more than a year, he eventually came to believe that Patsy did really hear her voices and that they were indeed meaningful to her.

For Marius this was a big step, as he was effectively walking away from the accepted mainstream medical view of what voices meant (e.g. nothing), and on the say so of one of his patients was prepared to let go of what his own psychiatric training had taught him. Instead he took his lead from Patsy, a diagnosed schizophrenic, because what she had said made more sense then any other theory he had heard. At some risk then he decided to try to do something positive with this new perspective. Thus began a journey that continues to this day, a journey that crucially has always involved voice hearers and others finding out together what this experience might mean and how it might be overcome.

The importance of listening

It is important to stress that the hearing voices movement can be said to have started by simply asking voice hearers what their voices were saying to them and what was it like to hear them. This may seem like a rather strange claim to make, but at the time no one was interested in what it was like to hear voices. When Professor Marius Romme, the Dutch psychiatrist started to ask people who heard voices about their experiences and what they meant to them, many of his colleagues thought he was crazy. The reason for this strong reaction was that at the time people who heard voices were told to ignore them, after all they were "hallucinations" and therefore meaningless.

To be told that the voices are just a symptom of an illness, when those voices are as real to you as anything else in the physical world is very dis-empowering. Take this common personal experience as an example:

George hears voices continuously. The voices are sometimes pleasant, but at other times they say unpleasant things and they interrupt him when he would prefer to concentrate on something happening in the purely physical world, such as an interesting meeting. Often he tries to discuss these voices with members of the medical profession. He wants to discuss what the voices say and the significance of the voices, but he is told they are just a symptom of his illness, to be ignored as best he may. However, he does hear voices that talk about things deeply relevant and meaningful to him. How can he believe that these voices are part of an illness and of no more significance than a sore throat? In an environment where there is active discouragement to talk about the voices from the medical advisors, George is being asked to accept that his own experiences are not relevant.

Right from the beginning people who heard voices told us that this discouraging approach and the treatment that followed really did not help them to understand or cope with their voices any better. It was for this reason we set out to discover more about why this was and what sort of things might help them more. The key word is LISTENING, listening to what people tell us and then developing ways of working based on this information.

The hearing voices movement then, was founded on the principle of finding new and better ways to help voice hearers troubled by their experience to change their relationships and attitudes to their voices. The first goal was to find ways of helping people who heard voices to take up their lives again. The second goal was to make sure that what we learnt was well known to family members, friends and professionals and wider society. We have always looked for ways to increase everyone's understanding of the experience of hearing voices and to challenge the false impressions and ideas that many people have about voices. We have always believed that if society changes its attitude to voices then psychiatry is much more like to follow.

Table II: Voice Hearing Questionnaire:

The questionnaire was originally designed as a research tool to elicit information from people who hear voices. It has proved to be extremely useful in getting a much fuller picture of the shared experiences of voice hearers and the results have subsequently been used to develop a range of coping strategies that can help voice hearers to come to terms with their experience.

As a result of using the questionnaire, we discovered that as well as its value for research, it also proved to be a good way of beginning the process of exploring the voice experience for individual voice hearers – and – as a means of developing the confidence of mental health workers who want to work with voice hearers.

It is important to stress that the questionnaire was developed by voice hearers in partnership with mental health professionals and that voice hearers are regarded as being the experts and full partners in the process of finding solutions to the difficulties that hearing voices can sometimes cause.

You can find out more about the questionnaire and download a copy here
http://www.intervoiceonline.org/2006/12/20/voice-hearing-a-questionnaire

Developed by Sandra Escher, Patsy Hage and Marius Romme. Further revisions by Monique Pennings.

One of the most significant discoveries we made was that there were some people who heard voices who did not have a problem with them – they could cope with their voices. This was something that was not generally known and certainly not within mental health services, this is unsurprising as obviously they did not get to see any voice hearers that could cope.

The next thing we tried to find out was why it was that some people could cope with the experience and others could not? Again, we asked the people who were best able to provide the answers, the voice hearers themselves including psychiatric patients, and equally importantly, people who heard voices who had never needed to seek the assistance of psychiatric services. What we discovered was that those people who are not able to cope with their voices, on the whole have not been able to cope with the traumatic events that lay at the root of their voice hearing experience.

Another important principle that has informed the work of the hearing voices movement is that we make sure the ways of helping we develop have been developed by voice hearers and professionals working together. We believe this has been one of the most important factors in the success of our approach and it means that in the hearing voices movement everybody (people who hear voices, workers, family and friends) are all considered an expert of their own experiences. What we mean when we say this is that we see each other first as people, secondly as equal partners and thirdly as all having different but mutually valuable expertise to offer. This can either be through direct experience of hearing voices or having lived with, being friends of or having worked with voice hearers.

By developing our work in this way and by being open

to everyone's ideas and interpretations we have reached the conclusion that it is very important to try to understand the meaning and the significance of the voices for you – what are they trying to tell you? We can say this with some confidence, because we have met a lot of voice hearers who have recovered from the stress caused by their voices.

Marius Romme and Sandra Escher in association with many researchers and Hearing Voices Networks across the world have carried out research over the last twenty two years. Marius says of the work:

> "What this research shows is that we must accept that the voices exist. We must also accept that we cannot change the voices. They are not curable, just as you cannot cure left-handedness – human variations are not open to cure – only to coping. Therefore to assist people to cope we should not give them therapy that does not work. We should let people decide for themselves what helps or not. It takes time for people to accept that hearing voices is something that belongs to them."

Sandra Escher meanwhile, organises annual conferences for voice hearers and professionals and uses her journalistic skills to ensure coverage in newspapers, magazines and the electronic media with the objective of opening up discussion in society as a whole about what voices mean and to try to generate more tolerance and understanding of people who are distressed by this experience. Her particular interest is the experiences of children who hear voices and in 1993 she organised a special conference in Amsterdam for 27 children and their parents, all of whom made contact as a result of media coverage. It was held, imaginatively I thought, at the city zoo and the success of the event led to Sandra undertaking a research project exploring the particular experience of 80 children who hear voices, the research project was started in 1995 and has recently been completed (see section on Children who hear voices).

There are now voice hearing networks and support groups active in twenty-one countries. An increasing number of researchers, practitioners, people hearing voices and family members have been influenced by this experience-based approach and have become involved in research, training and all forms of support. The basic premise is that voices are related to and influenced by the life experiences of the voice hearer. An important outcome of this experiential approach is that growing numbers of voice hearers have discovered their own ability to recover.

Why "Hearing Voices"

We have for a long time recognised the inadequacy of restricting the range of 'psychic' experiences such as visions, tactile sensations and other sensory experiences to the limiting term 'hearing voices'. It is primarily a problem of language and replacing the pathologising terms used by psychiatry with its 'hallucinations, delusions and psychoses' with something more empowering. The term 'hearing voices' has the advantage of being recognisable as it is often used by people, it is a direct and neutral term which is why it was easy to adopt it. We are interested in the broad range of phenomenon and are currently trying to reconstruct "psychosis" in the same we have with the word 'auditory hallucination", it is not an easy task though.

It is also important to remember that terms such as

hallucinations and delusions are based on a value judgement made by psychiatrists and are certainly not clinical descriptions of states of mind or symptoms of a disease. For instance one person's beliefs can be another's delusions. It is difficult to determine what is the truth as the terms are applied selectively, for instance respected scientists false beliefs are rarely called delusions. Secondly, usually other grounds are applied to justify using descriptions such as delusions and hallucinations, such as low, devalued or degraded social status – or – because of the anxieties and concerns of those people around the person having the unusual experience.

Thirdly, there is no difference in the way "normal" people form their imaginings and beliefs and the way those who have been diagnosed as schizophrenic construct their delusions and hallucinations. Psychiatrists who use terms such as hallucinations and delusions never consider their importance to the life story of the person who has these experiences or beliefs. Recent research shows that the so called auditory hallucinations of psychiatric patients are actually meaningful and make sense in terms of their lives and how they cope.

Professor Marius Romme gets a shock and founds a movement

Patsy had got some of her ideas about voices from the theories of an American psychologist, Julian Haynes who wrote a book called 'The Origins of Consciousness and the Breakdown of the Bi-camera Mind[22]. The Iliad is a book

22. Jaynes J: *The origin of consciousness and the breakdown of the bicameral mind*: (1976) Houghton Mifflin, Boston

written by the ancient poet, Homer. It tells of the Trojan Wars, a war caused by the most beautiful woman in the world, Helen. She left her husband and ran off to Troy with Paris. Her husband pursued her with all the armies of Greece and Homer wrote the Iliad about the war that followed. Homer frequently describes some Greek god or goddess appearing to a warrior in the middle of the Trojan War and telling him to do something. Julian Jaynes argues persuasively in his book that, when that happened it was not a metaphorical experience but a real one. The warrior really saw the goddess and heard her words. Jaynes believes that up until about 1300 BC, and before the development of written language, hearing voices was common to all humanity and the experience was all but eradicated by what we now know as consciousness. The people who hear voices today are carriers of an evolutionary residue from this ancient time.

Romme accepted Patsy's voices and as a consequence invited other people to talk about their experience, and found that although they could talk about their experience they could not help each other. Then Marius and Patsy appeared on a Dutch television programme and talked about voice hearing, asking for people who heard voices to phone in. 450 people rang, and of those 150 people said they were able to cope with their voices without assistance from psychiatry, indeed in some cases were happy to hear voices. This finding was most surprising and it led to a crucial question. Perhaps the techniques employed by those who coped well with their voices could be used by those who did not? Marius began the study of voice hearers experiences, which continues to this day. He did two more things. He assisted the founding of a movement of voice hearers and organised a conference in order to encourage a broader discussion to change the attitude of society and to try to change the way the voice hearers were treated by the medical profession and especially psychiatrists. Marius recalls

"It was Patsy Hage, who made it clear to me that the psychiatric approach was not very helpful. Because as a traditional trained clinician I was only interested in her voice hearing experience as far as it concerned the characteristics of a hallucination, in order to construct a diagnosis in combination with other symptoms. But she was interested in the voices and the power they exerted over her; in the stress she experienced; in what they told to her etc. She did not like my reductionist approach. She was hindered by her voices and medication did not work with her. And as a result she became more and more isolated because the voices forbid her all kind of social activities.

In order to break through this isolation, I suggested she should talk to another patient who also heard voices. First she felt some resistance to the idea, but eventually she accepted the proposal as we did not know of another way to learn more about hearing voices. I also realised that I did not know much about the experience of hearing voices. So I organised a meeting and the patients who attended were very enthusiastic about talking about their voices. They recognised each others experience. However, after some contacts they, as well as I, realised that they still did not know how to cope with their voices, because all the patients I knew were more or less powerless against their voices.

To solve this problem we asked for help from a TV talk show. We wanted to meet somebody who not only heard voices, but also was able to cope with them. In

this talk show the patient told her story and I asked if there was somebody who knew how to cope with the voices to contact us. To our astonishment 700 people reacted. To organise the information we constructed a questionnaire together with Patsy Hage. From those who returned the questionnaire we selected people who could explain clearly what they did in coping with their voices. This was the beginning of our new understanding of the meaning of voices."

How did it start in the UK?

I wanted to emphasise this starting point as it had a powerful effect on me and did so to other people I talked to in England about this new way of thinking about voices. I left the Netherlands with this challenge from Marius to develop the work in the UK:

"I ask you to try to do the same in England. Groups need to be established in each country where people can talk together about hearing voices.... it takes groups of people with the same experience to change attitudes...in America and England now, psychiatrists are following the needs of parent organisations. My goal is not changing psychiatry, not changing parents, but offering people hearing voices an organisation from which they can emancipate themselves. You have to organise groups, and then psychiatry follows." (Marius Romme in interview with the author in November 1988)

He also said (I think with his tongue in his cheek) that it was possible that hearing voices by so called "normal"

31

people was something unique to the Dutch and he was curious to discover if any British people heard them too – as it happened they did.

The movement in the UK took its inspiration from the Netherlands, where, it started with the establishment of a national network for voice hearers set up in 1987 at the first conference for voice hearers held in Utrecht. At the conference voice hearers decided to start an association to stimulate more interest in the subject, as at that time not much was known about the experience of hearing voices. They formed WEERLANK (best translated as "Resonance") open to voice hearers (both within psychiatry and those who have had no contact with psychiatry), relatives, friends and professionals. Their goal was to break down the taboo of voice hearing by promoting acceptance of voices and the emancipation of voice hearers; to help break down the isolation of voice hearers and to help them cope better with their experiences and to encourage a change of attitude in the medical profession of their understanding and treatment of voices. During the last twenty two years Weerlank has set up self-help groups; a telephone support network; publishes a newsletter and is actively disseminating information and guidance about voice hearing.

In the UK, the new way of working began as a small planning group originating in Manchester, the first UK Hearing Voices Group was formed in 1988 and was modelled on the Dutch self help group. In 1989 the Manchester group organised a speaking tour in the North of England for Marius Romme and Sandra Escher. The meetings were very well attended by voice hearers, their relatives, and interested professionals. This was the first of many visits and exchanges. Knowledge of the work was then spread by the publication of articles in specialist magazines and journals, local newspapers and the national media and the book, Accepting Voices written and edited by Marius Romme and Sandra Escher and published by Mind publications in 1993. In August 1995 the first international conference on the subject was held in the Maastricht, Netherlands. Thereafter England was the first country, and Manchester the first city to pick up this idea and became one of the most organised and most active in the world.

From this beginning there has been a gradual development of hearing voices networks over Europe. First in Finland, in Italy, Portugal, Sweden and Germany and now there is activity and networks in 22 countries through out the world. A new way of thinking about hearing voices and even more importantly, a new way of helping people who are troubled by their voices is being developed.

What is the significance of the hearing voices moment for voice hearers?

There are many theories held by psychiatry about what may cause voices, many of them presume that it is part of a psychosis and that it might be caused by some kind of genetic flaw. Psychiatrists, nurses, and other mental health professionals have been taught to regard voices as an auditory hallucination and it is usually thought to be part of the symptoms that make up illnesses like schizophrenia. The treatment for people troubled by their voices is most often medication (like neuroleptics/anti-psychotics), which can in some cases reduce the anxiety caused by the voices but sometimes at the cost of making the person feel sluggish or restless. In some cases the medication can lead to irreversible side effects if taken in high doses over long periods of time.

Generally though, within psychiatry, it is presumed that there is not a lot an individual can do for themselves to cope with their voices, besides sticking to their medical regime. Indeed, many professionals are taught not to engage voice hearers about the content of their voice experience as this is thought to be "buying in" to the patients delusions and therefore unhelpful. Most often professionals will seek to distract the voice hearer from their voices. As you will probably realise by now we do not believe this is a helpful approach.

Here are some of the problems that voice hearers have told us about their experience of mainstream psychiatric practice:

• Many people who hear voices and have become psychiatric patients have concluded that their experience of hearing voices has been wrongly interpreted as a symptom of a psychiatric illness, such as schizophrenia.

• Many voice hearers who have become psychiatric patients have told us they are discouraged and sometimes prevented from talking about their voices. They have realised that this has become a barrier to their understanding of what is happening for them and finding their own answers to their problems

• Many voice hearers who become patients are treated with high doses of neuroleptics which leads to people getting stuck and unable to move on, preventing the possibility of them being able to regain control of their lives.

Therefore many voice hearers are glad that opportunities have been created by the hearing voices movement to explore their voice experience and where their experiences are recognised and accepted as real and where you can talk about this experience and be accepted.

PART 2: PEOPLE WHO HEAR VOICES

Table III: Some famous people who claimed they heard voices:

Alexander the Great (Emperor)
Joan of Arc (martyr and saint)
Teresa of Avila (religious mystic and saint) Beethoven (composer)
William Blake (artist)
Caesar (Emperor)
Calvin (religious leader)
Charlemagne (Emperor)
Columbus (discoverer)
Charles Dickens (writer)
Philip K. Dick (writer)
George Fox (Quakers)
Mahatma Gandhi (politician/ pacifist)
Anthony Hopkins (actor)
Jesus (prophet)
Carl Jung (psychologist)
Malcolm Lowry (writer)
Martin Luther (religious leader)
Mohammed (prophet)
Sylvia Plath (poet)
Jonathan Swift (writer)
John Paul Sartre (writer)
Joseph Smith (Mormons)
Socrates (philosopher)
Swedenborg (philosopher/politician)
Zoe Wannamaker (actress)
Evelyn Waugh (writer)
John Wellesley (founder of Methodism)
Virginia Woolf (writer)

For a far longer list and descriptions of the experiences of well known people who heard voices visit the INTERVOICE website at www.intervoiceonline.org

Hearing voices in history and religion

There are, it may be, so many different kinds of voices in the world, and none of them is without significance

St. Paul to the Corinthians

Some years ago Sandra Escher wrote an article based on her research of the experience of hearing voices through the ages. Sandra found that the experiences of hearing voices from a source that no one else can perceive has been reported throughout history, right back to the ancient civilisations of Egypt, Rome, Babylon, Tibet and Greece. She says that in these earliest societies positive voices were commonly reported and it was believed that at certain sacred sites it was possible to obtain advice and guidance for important decisions from the voice of a God. In later times it was more common that these divine messages were mediated through appointed priests or priestesses and in different ways throughout the history of humanity the idea of voices as messengers has remained, even to this day.

One of the earliest recorded experiences of hearing voices is from the Greek philosopher Socrates (469-399 BC), who reported he heard the voice of a daemon which he valued as a helpful guide. He said that he let his life be directed by this daemon, which he regarded as a voice of wisdom and which he did not experience as an aspect of his own thoughts.

However, he also knew there could be problems with this experience and wrote that it was possible for clairvoyant perception to coincide with madness: in other words he understood, two and a half thousand years ago, that a person in the midst of such perception is understandably ill adjusted to the routine demands of every day space and time. You may know that Socrates was eventually persecuted for his ideas and was put on trial which ultimately led to his death, at this time he said of his voice:

"You may have heard me speak of an oracle or sign which comes to me, which my accuser Melitus ridicules and sets out in the indictment. This sign I have had ever since I was a child. The sign is a voice which comes to me and always forbids me to do something which I am going to do, but never commands me to do anything, and this is what stands in the way of being a politician".

As Fred Johnson says in "The Anatomy of Hallucinations"[23] "The inclusion of voice hearing in the list of his crimes may well have been the beginning of a tradition in Western civilisation".

Furthermore, one of the first hypotheses to be made about voices and other experiences like visions came from another Greek philosopher, Aristotle (384-322 BC), according to Aristotle voices were produced by the same mechanism which normally produce hallucinations during sleep, being the same as the mechanism of dreaming[24]. It is interesting to note that theories about the meaning of voices have been with us a long time.

Of course experiences of voice hearing have always been closely associated with religious and spiritual experiences and one of the most common ideas about the origin of voices is that they came from God. It is significant that many people identified as founders of religious movements

23. Fred H. Johnson, *The Anatomy of Hallucinations*, Burnham Inc Pub (March 1978)

24.Joel Feinberg, *Doing and Deserving: Essays in the Theory of Responsibility* (1970)

reported hearing voices: Jesus (Christianity); Mohammed (Islam); George Fox (Quakers) and Joseph Smith (Mormons) amongst others. Both in the old and new testament there are accounts of people hearing voices; Moses, Jesus, the apostle Paul and Mary all declared they heard the voice of God or messengers from God.

There is the well-known episode when Moses heard the voice of God coming from a burning bush telling him to guide the Hebrews out of Egypt. Throughout the entire Jewish bible, God is found addressing humans in speech: he calls them to account, enters into dialogue with them, and listens to their questions, Christianity has also retained this concept of the personal God and consequently the mystical experience, has without exception, always been expressed in terms of a personal encounter, such as a conversation or a message. We certainly know that Jesus' contemporaries occasionally considered him to be possessed. It does make me wonder what psychiatrists would have made of an emaciated Jesus of Nazareth, following his forty day fast in the desert, his conversations with the devil and his subsequent attempted demolition of the Temple in Jerusalem. In fact, I have some idea, because in training sessions on the voice hearing experience for mental health workers we have used the experience above, somewhat disguised, and there is no doubt, he would have been sectioned under mental health legislation (for self neglect and personal endangerment, experiencing hallucinations, delusions of grandeur and an act of random violence against property and people).

On the other hand, Mohammed first heard a voice near Mecca as he was walking on his own and meditating, it said "Hail to thee, O messenger of God" and like many people who have this experience for the first time he looked around him to try and find where the voice came from, but he saw nothing. A few days later he had a vision of the Angel Gabriel who told him that God had chosen him to be a prophet and again his reaction was similar to other voice hearers in that he considered killing himself. He didn't, of course, and in the following years much of Mohammed's writings were inspired by voices and visions. In those parts of the world where Christianity, Islam and Judaism have dominated the idea has survived that the divine may be discovered within human consciousness. Up until the birth of psychology and psychiatry, the Catholic Church claimed the right to classify and judge these individuals according to four main diagnostic categories: canonization, possession, heresy and witchcraft.

Throughout the history of Christianity, the hearing of voices continued to play an important role, for instance the abbess Hildegard of Bingen, the Saints, Teresa of Avila and Francis of Assisi, and the founder of Protestantism, Martin Luther heard voices. Probably the best known voice-hearer is Joan of Arc, the young peasant woman whose role in the wars fought by France against the English is an early example of a voice hearer where political events determined how her experiences were interpreted. Initially, it was believed by her troops that she was guided by the voices of angels when she took them into battle. However when she was later captured by the English she was instead accused of witchcraft because of the voices. In fact her trial and execution was less about the origin of her voices but more about the political debate about who would hold the French crown and her life was sacrificed as a result.

Whether these inner revelations are testimony to their sanity or madness or rather lies outside of either of these states of mind, I leave to the reader's judgement. I don't intend to be disrespectful to those people who are of the Christian faith, in fact quite the opposite. Within this apparently flippant comment, lies a crucial question just how do we know who are the prophets and who the mad? and who makes the definitions?

Table IV: What does it feel like to hear voices?

What people tell us their voices are like:
• They may be coming out of the air.
• They may be in your head.
• They may be in your body.
• It may be your own voice.
• It may be the voice of someone else.
• There may be more than one voice.
• It may be a cross between a male and a female.
• They may be critical.
• They may be friendly.
• You may hear whistling or whining.
• They may vary in strength and frequency from day to day and over longer time periods

What people tell us that it feels like to hear voices:
Some people find voices are helpful, some do not.
Some positives:
• They can provide company.
• They may cheer you up and make you laugh.
• A "good voice" can help against "bad" one.
• They can help you to cope with bad things that happen in your life.
• They can give sexual enjoyment.
• They can make you feel special.
Some negatives:
• They can be very repetitive.
• They can cause paranoia.
• They can be upsetting.

What about disturbing beliefs?
Different people call this experience by different names. Doctors might call it "having delusions". Some people describe it as having "false beliefs" but we have chosen the term "disturbing beliefs" because this experience can disrupt and disturb your life. At the same time for some people these beliefs can be a comfort.

What they may be like:
• You may feel everyone else is out of step – not you.
• You may feel statements on TV or radio refer to yourself.
• You may feel that everyone is against you (sometimes called a persecution complex).

It's hard to explain

It is difficult to explain what it is like to hear "voices", particularly if you have never heard voices yourself. The word vocation, for instance means to "follow a calling", in other words to hear a voice and act on it. This is not what most people mean when they say they have a vocation, but that is the root meaning of the word. Indeed, many historically important people claimed to have heard a voice that acted as their inspiration (see Table II).

However, for many voice hearers, the voices might be present all day and have the effect of preventing them from doing things in their daily life. Voices might also punish the voice hearer if they do not do what the voice wants them to. Hearing voices is often regarded as dangerous because "voices" have been known to tell people to commit murders and to harm themselves, and there are sensational examples of this.

In a nutshell

There are many prejudices and difficulties to overcome if one attempts to explain. However, the experience of hearing voices is not as alien an experience as it is generally thought to be. Firstly, it may be the same as hearing a voice in the normal way through your ears, the difference being that the "voice" has no physical cause. But like normal voices there is variety, and every experience has its differences. For example; leaving a party on their say so; not being able to talk about the voices; becoming silent, and as a result, isolated from other people. You may think you have never experienced this, but are you sure? You may have had the experience of hearing someone call your name only to find that there is no one there. Indeed, research shows that, especially for people recently bereaved, it is not an uncommon experience to hear the voice of the recently deceased person. That is not the only explanation of what it is like. As well as hearing voices through the ears, people also hear voices as if they are thoughts entering the mind from somewhere outside themselves. This is not the same as a suddenly inspired idea, which people usually recognise as coming from themselves, rather the thoughts are not their own and would seem to come from outside their own consciousness, like telepathy.

A good example of this is the experience of recalling a rhyme or tune, which you find yourself repeating unconsciously under your breath and which keeps going through your head again and again. You can even find yourself humming it. You never took a decision to start thinking of it and it is difficult to stop thinking about it. The difference between the tune and "voice thought" which appears as words in your mind is that it may go on to speak coherently to you and even engage you in conversation. You, yourself are not responsible for it and you have no idea what this "voice" is going to say next.

Thoughts without words. Visions, smells, tastes and dreams...

There are many different ways to hear voices. Voices can be experienced inside the head, from outside the head, or even in the body. It may be one voice or many voices. The voice may talk to you or about you. There are other ways to hear voices, some of them make the phrase "hearing voices" a poor description and perhaps one day we will have to come up with a better one – because it is never the same for everyone. Some people, for instance, experience non-verbal thoughts, images and visions, tastes, smells and touch. All with no physical cause and all sensations they did not call into being themselves.

Voices can be like dreams. We all dream and experience words, images, and even sensations. When we are bored we can drift off and have a short dream. When we dream all sorts of strange things can happen to us, but we still believe they're really happening to us. Hearing voices can be like that – a waking dream – but something that is experienced as real.

What do the voices tell you and what can they do?

What voices do
Voices can vary from the very pathological and undesirable to being considered a faculty or gift. Many people, even

those troubled by their voices would not like to stop hearing voices – voices may be pathological for some people but they may also fill a useful psychological function.

Lots of different voices

What do voices say? What messages do they bring? Usually there is not just one "voice" that says the same sort of things all the time. There can be a number of voices that may be different from each other. One could say pleasant things and be on your side while another might not. Sometimes a voice can have a complete personality and be instantly recognised by the person hearing the voice as some particular person, dead or alive, or some known spirit or being such as God or the Devil. Other voices may not have much of a personality and the person hearing what is said may not put it down to some particular person or being. Hearing the "voice" is like hearing random snatches of conversation.

The worst news:

Some "voices" are more pleasant than others. The less pleasant ones may abuse the person hearing them, saying that this person is no good, of no account, evil, stupid, worthless. They may say this sort of thing monotonously and continually. The voices may also give people orders that they felt they have to obey because the voices control the person's body. For example, the voices might also cause them to have a fit, or experience pain.

Still not good

Alternatively, the voices could simply be constantly or occasionally interrupting with meaningless and valueless comments, such as "that's not a good idea", "that's not going to work", "he's one of them" and so on. The voices may also discuss something with apparent omniscience and wisdom – apparently they know everything – but the voice hearer can find that the information is false. For example, the voices tell you that if you send someone a letter asking for something, that person will do what you want. When it does not happen it can be very disillusioning.

The good news
There can be a pleasant side to hearing voices (see Positive Voices below). Sometimes the apparent wisdom is real and the voices, or some of them, can seem intelligent. Voice hearers report that they have been told things they did not know or could not work out for themselves and the voices have been of real assistance. For some people this experience is considered a gift, something that is like a valuable insight or even extra sensory perception (ESP), and the voices can be trusted. Voices can be intelligent, witty, funny and incisive. They can in themselves be a coping mechanism. What the voices say corresponds with the effect that the social and emotional world is having on the voice hearer. The voices will often comment on how the voice hearer is experiencing the world and in this way the voices can be a defence mechanism against overwhelming or forbidden feelings. Voices are often related to life history, such as recent or childhood trauma and the voices speak of powerlessness and injustice.

Voices and their relationship with the voice hearer

Based on what voice hearers tell us we believe hearing voices can be regarded as a meaningful, real (although sometimes painful, fearful and overwhelming) event, that speak to the person in a metaphorical way about their lives, emotions and environment. Marius Romme and Sandra Escher discovered that people experiencing distress as a consequence of abusive or commanding voices can often recognise their voices as those of their actual abusers and the voices have the effect of attacking their sense of self-esteem and worth. However, it should not be forgotten that some people experience helpful and guiding voices, also arising from times of trauma and stress (more about this below). Having discovered these kinds of relationships they next step is too develop techniques to assist voice hearers focus on their experience and get to know their voices better.

This is in contradiction to most psychiatric and psychological orthodoxies that assume that such psycho-pathological symptoms are not open to insight and talking treatments and instead would attempt to distract patients with such symptoms from their voices. This turns out not only to be bad advice, but actually counter productive, as such approaches dis-empower the voice hearer by denying to them their real experience and disarming them from taking on the voices and standing up for themselves. The new approach requires the voice hearer to make space for the voices, to listen but not to necessarily follow, to engage, but in their own time and space essentially to learn how to control them in their own terms, according to their own beliefs and explanatory framework. This acceptance of the voices is crucial to growth and resolution, voice hearers who have learnt these techniques can now say "I hear voices, they are part of me and I am glad they are".

Exploring the meaning of voices

It became evident that it was important to explore the relationship between the hearing of voices and the life history of the voice hearer in order to see if it was possible to help them to solve their emotional and other problems. This approach emphasises the importance of understanding what the voices were saying to the voice hearer and required them to focus their attention on the voices as a way of finding a resolution to the difficulties they caused. In doing so, however, it was considered very important to develop a way of working that was cooperative and based on mutual trust. As a result Professor Romme, Sandra Escher and the Maastricht team investigated the following features of the voice hearing experience:

- the identity of the voices;
- the characteristics of their communication with the person;
- the way of talking;
- the age of the voices;
- what they have to say;
- what triggers the appearance of the voices;
- what important changes in the life of the voice hearer were related to the appearance of the voices;
- characteristics of the voice hearer's upbringing and any special experiences that occurred in childhood.

What triggers voices?

As a result of this research, carried out using questionnaires and one to one interviews it was discovered that voices are triggered when experiencing certain threatening or overwhelming emotions such as:

- insecurity
- fear
- aggression
- ones own sexual feelings
- the sexual feelings of others
- losing control or when confronted by certain situations (feeling out of control or losing control) such as new situations
- unexpected situations
- the company of new people
- situations that create stress
- the feelings of others in the same room
- fatigue etc.

Table V: Hearing voices amongst "normal people"

Many people hear voices and have never been a psychiatric patient, this is already a well known but neglected fact.

It has been known for some time that a high percentage of the general population experience brief and occasional voices, particularly at times of bereavement, divorce and separation. It is also the case for people in extreme circumstances, for instance, 80 per cent of those who have endured torture have hallucinated during their ordeal[25] and the phenomenon is also seen amongst long-distance yachtsmen[26]. In cases like these, there is no evidence

---

25. FE Somnier and IK Genefke, *Psychotherapy for victims of torture*, The British Journal of Psychiatry 149: 323-329 (1986)

26. G Bennet, *Accidents and fatigue in small boats*, British Medical Journal, (1972)

of the presence of mental illness – indeed, often quite the contrary.

More recent epidemiological research in Baltimore, in a population of 15,000 people, found that 10-15 per cent of those interviewed reported that they had heard voices over a long period of time, only a third of those interviewed reported experiencing negative effects[27].

Further research in 1991 revealed that many cases of hearing voices did not meet the criteria for a psychiatric diagnosis[28]. Significantly, Romme's latest research of both non-patient and patient voice hearers has shown that both groups hear negative and positive voices at about the same level. The difference is mainly in how the two groups react to their voices, with the non-patients not experiencing fear of the voices and experiencing far less upset from them than the patients.

Voices are heard by "normal people" and can be sometimes be a positive experience

As I said earlier, throughout human history, there have been descriptions of the 'voice within' in religion, in the occult; magical and mystical descriptions; historical, psychological, fictional and mythical. The psychological literature on these experiences has largely focused on individuals considered to be "mad", while the religious literature concentrates on those thought to be divinely or demoniacally inspired or possessed. Unsurprisingly perhaps, little attention has been given to the inner voice experience of people who fall into

27. A. Y. Tien, Distribution of hallucinations in the population, Journal Social Psychiatry and Psychiatric Epidemiology (1991)

28. W. W Eaton, A Romanoski, JC Anthony, G Nestadt, Screening for psychosis in the general population with a self-report interview. The Journal of nervous and mental disease (1991)

neither of these groups.

However, there is growing body of research into this issue, in fact surprisingly this research began over 100 years ago. As long ago as 1889, Henry Sidgewick was commissioned by the Society of Psychical Research to conduct the "International Census of Waking Hallucinations in the Sane" and to carry out interviews with a large group of ordinary people, over the next three years his team of researchers interviewed 17,000 adults from England, Russia and Brazil were surveyed asking them:

"Have you ever, when believing yourself to be completely awake, had a vivid impression of seeing or being touched by a living being or inanimate object, or of hearing a voice ; which impression, so far as you could discover, was not due to any external cause."

Nearly 10% reported they had experienced an unexplained perception, 2.9% of the total reported having heard a voice. Those who responded positively were then followed up for more detail about their experience. The study found that there were large numbers of voice hearers[29].

Over a hundred years later, in a sort of follow up study to Sidgewick's, a large scale survey of 15,000 people in Baltimore, St Louis and Los Angeles was carried out by Professor Allen Y Tien, he found that voices are heard regularly and continuously by 2.3% of the general population. Further research in 1991 by W. Eaton revealed that many cases of hearing voices did not meet the criteria for a psychiatric diagnosis and therefore were "normal".

In the last twenty years there has been more research on the experience of voices amongst normal people, including

29. Sidgewick H.A. (1894) Report on the census of hallucinations, Proceedings of the Society of Psychical Research, No. 26, pp. 25 394

research by Posey and Losch[30], Myrtle Heery[31], and Vanessa Beavan[32] (see below) and others which has confirmed that voice hearing is as commonly experienced today. These studies included groups of students (including one of medical students), lone sailors and survivors of torture. They show that many of us have have had or will have such experiences at some time in our life (often following traumatic events such as bereavement, loss and major life changes).

There is an excellent book on this subject called *Hearing Voices – A Common Human Experience* by John Watkins[33], a mental health counsellor and educator from Australia. This thoroughly researched book shows that although hearing voices is often considered a hallmark of madness it is actually a rather common experience. John points out that while "voices" are a prominent symptom of psychotic disorders like schizophrenia they can also occur in many other contexts. He found that many well-adjusted individuals have had at least one memorable voice experience and some people have them regularly and whilst some experiences are disturbing others provide comfort, reassurance, and guidance. These "benign" inner voices often occur in association with non-ordinary states

30. Posey T.B. and Losch M.E. (1984), *Auditory hallucinations of hearing voices in 375 normal subjects*, Imagination, Cognition and Personality, vol. 3, no.2, pp. 99 113

31. Heery M. W. (1989): *Inner Voice Experiences: an exploratory study of 30 cases*, Journal of Transpersonal Psychiatry, vol. 21, no. 1, pp. 73 82

32. Vanessa Beavan, John Read and Claire Cartwright (2006) *Angels at our tables: A summary of the findings from a 3-year research project into New Zealanders' Experiences of Hearing Voices*, University of Auckland, New Zealand

33. Watkins J, *Hearing Voices – A Common Human Experience* (2008) Michelle Anderson Publishing, Australia

of consciousness, mystical and paranormal phenomena, near-death experiences, and shamanistic practices and may serve as a vehicle for creative inspiration, extrasensory communication, the call of vocation, and spiritual revelation.

Positive Voices

It is also the case that people hear positive voices that cause them no problems and it is important to emphasise this point. For instance in 2006 researchers from the University of Newcastle Upon Tyne in the UK looked into the experience of hearing voices as a positive experience. They found that the content or frequency of hearing voices was not the primary difference between positive and negative voice hearing experiences[34]. They concluded

"...a positive voice experience could say unpleasant things, and a negative voice could say apparently nice comments. Rather positive voices were seen to play a greater role in providing companionship, comfort and support. Positive voices were seen to be more helpful than harmful whereas negative voices were the opposite way and seen as more harmful than helpful. Negative voices were seen to be less controllable. In both negative and positive voices it was difficult to stop the voice from talking, but was easier to have a conversation with a positive voice experience. As with previous research positive voices were engaged more than resisted, and negative voices were resisted more than engaged."

Other recent research from across the world includes that of psychologist Vanessa Beavan from the University

---

34. Positive Experiences of Voices: Elisa Gatiss et al, University of Newcastle Upon Tyne (2006)

of Aukland, New Zealand, published in 2006. Vanessa gathered answers from 154 voice-hearers by questionnaire and interviewed 50 of them. She discovered that hearing voices is more complex than suggested by the psychiatric model of voices as a symptom of severe mental illness as voice-hearers reported a diverse range of experiences and explanatory models and most had never been diagnosed with a psychiatric disorder. Further, while 54 per cent had been in contact with mental health services, only 22 per cent said it was for reasons "at least somewhat related to their voice experiences".

Here are some examples of the experiences reported by voice hearers:

- Positive voice content included hearing advice, encouraging and comforting words, and giggling. On the darker side, negative content could be crying, criticism or commands to hurt themselves or others.
- More than half identified a single event, mostly negative, happening shortly before they first heard a voice, yet, over time, participants' emotional reactions to their voices became more commonly positive than negative.
- Voices of deceased people were the most common; others included parts of the self, gods and aliens.
- People attributed their voices to causes like brain dysfunction, drugs, trauma and spiritual entities.
- Many participants wanted voice-hearing to be considered normal, to reduce the stigma they experienced.
- Many experienced them when waking or falling asleep, or if someone close had recently died.
- The voices were mostly friendly or helpful for 48 per cent, mostly negative or unhelpful for 25 per cent, neutral

for 15 per cent and varied greatly for the rest. 54 per cent had been in

- contact with mental health services.
- Around 25 per cent heard voices talking or arguing with each other.

Another study published in 2004 found that for some people who hear voices the experience can be pleasurable (26%). The authors pointed out that "This finding challenges our understanding of auditory hallucinations as a per se negative experience."[35]

Children and Young People who Hear Voices

Dr. Sandra Escher is a researcher, along with Marius Romme, she is the co-founder of the hearing voices movement, she is an expert on the issue of children and young people who hear voices, she has spent the last fifteen years talking to children who hear voices and to their parents and carers. Sandra has carried out the most detailed and thorough research into the phenomenon in the world to date. She has developed a new perspective on what the voices may represent and how you can help your child cope if they are hearing voices.

Sandra argues it is possible to find new and more empowering ways of thinking about children's experiences and that is is possible to find ways to assist children in their emotional development and recovery from hearing overwhelming voices. So, here are some simple common sense things that you can do to help your child.

---

35. Sanjuan J, Gonzalez JC, Aguilar EJ, Leal C and Os J; Acta Psychiatrica Scandinavica 2004

Table VI: What you can do if your child tells you they are hearing voices: A 10-point check-list

1. Try not to over react, although you will be understandably worried, work hard not to communicate your anxiety to your child.
2. Accept the reality of the voice experience for your child: Ask them about their voices, how long they have been hearing them, who or what they are, do they have names, what they say etc.
3. Let your child know that lots of children hear voices and mostly they go away after a while.
4. Even if the voices do not disappear your child can learn to live in harmony with his/her voices
5. It is important to breakdown your child's sense of isolation and differentness from other children. Your child is special, unusual perhaps, but normal.
6. Find out if your child has any difficulties or problems that they are finding very hard to cope with and work on trying to fix these problems. Think back to when the voices first started, what was happening to your child when they first heard voices? When did the voices arise for the first time? Was there anything unusual or stressful that might have occurred?
7. If you think you need outside help, find a therapist who is prepared to accept your child's experience and work with your child in a systematic way to understanding and cope with their voices better.
8. Be ready to listen to your child if they want to talk about their voices and use drawing, painting, acting and other creative ways to help them describe what is happening to them.
9. Get on with your lives and try not to let the voice experience become the centre of your child's life and your own.
10. Most children who live well with their voices have supportive families living around them who accept the experience as part of who their child is. You can do this too!

PART 3: WHAT TO DO ABOUT VOICES THAT CAUSE YOU PROBLEMS

If you hear voices that speak about you or to you, especially in a derogatory manner and tell a psychiatrist then you shouldn't really be surprised that they will probably regard you as having one of the main symptoms of schizophrenia or some other serious psychiatric illness. Psychiatrists are trained to identify the form that the voice experience takes, from their point of view if you hear "people" speaking to you who aren't there then you are hallucinating – and for them that is the significant issue – it is however, not a concern of theirs what the voices say. This is because psychiatry is preoccupied with the way the physical condition of the brain effects the way you think, therefore if your thoughts are causing problems then there might be something physically wrong with the brain.

Psychiatry has not thought very deeply about this phenomenon and has shown very little interest in the past in the nature of the voice hearing experience. Generally, it is only interested in the self reporting of "auditory hallucinations' as an indicator or symptom of a disease state. It has not considered the nature of the experience and rarely asks people who hear the voices what they mean to them. Further, they have never been interested in the narrative of the voice experience. One of the reasons for this is that they have never looked at hallucinations except in distressed people overcome by their experiences.

Our work has led us to believe that it is important to try to find meaning in your voice hearing experiences. This may sound radical, but is based on sound research involving questionnaires and interviews conducted with many voice hearers, both within and outside of psychiatry. Surprisingly, but it appears that voice hearers can cope with their voices (or conversely don't) not because of the content of the voice experience (which can be either abusive and devaluing or guiding and inspiring – or both) but as a result of the kind of relationship you have with the voices. Bottom line, this means that if you believe the voices to be in control you can't cope – if you believe you are stronger then the voices are, you can.

Table VII: Three phases found among people who hear voices

The startling phase
- Most voice hearers describe the onset of the experience as being quite sudden, startling and anxiety provoking, and can vividly remember
- the precise moment they first heard a voice.
- The age of the onset of the initial experience of voices varies widely, as does the intensity of the startling phase, which appears to be most severe when it occurs during adolescence. The confusion seems to be less when voices are heard from an early age, or did not make an appearance until later in adulthood (In a survey 6 per cent heard voices before the age of 6; 10 per cent between 10 and 20; 74 per cent after 20).
- Voices are often triggered by traumatic or emotional events such as accidents, divorce or bereavement, illnesses, psychotherapy sessions.

The impact of the voices fall into two types:
Some people perceive the voices as helpful and they evoke a feeling of recognition. These people feel the purpose of the voices is strengthening them and raising their self-esteem. The voices are experienced as positive and as an understandable aspect of their internal selves.

Others experience the voices as aggressive and negative from the very beginning. For these people the voices are hostile and are not accepted as part of themselves. They suffer from negative voices that can cause chaos in their minds, demanding so much attention that communication with the outside world is extremely difficult.

The phase of organisation: coping with the voices

Voice hearers often become confused by their voices and want to escape from them. For some, this urge lasts only a short time (weeks or months), for others, it can be many years. However, to come to terms with the voices on any level or to organise them successfully, requires some form of acceptance to take place. Denying the voices does not work. During this phase, voice hearers understandably seek ways of controlling or coping with the voices, strategies include:

- ignoring the voices (distraction)
- listening to them selectively
- entering into willing dialogue with them
- making specific appointments with them

Attempts at distraction and ignoring rarely work, although this is a strategy many voice hearers attempt, it seems the effort involved often leads to a severe restriction of life style. Unsurprisingly, initial feelings of panic and powerlessness are replaced with a period of anger at the voices, this anger does not appear to be part of a useful coping strategy. The most useful strategy described by voice hearers is to select the positive voices and listen and talk only to them, and to try to understand them.

An important element in coping successfully with voices is to accept them. This appears to be related to a process of growth towards taking
responsibility for one's own decisions. You have to learn to think in a positive way about yourself, your voices, and your own problems. Another strategy is to set limits and structure the contact with the voices, sometimes accompanied by rituals or repeated actions.

The phase of stabilisation

People can and do learn to cope with their voices and find a kind of equilibrium. In this state of balance, people consider the voices as part of themselves and their lives, and capable of a positive influence. During this phase, the individual is able to choose between following the advice of the voices or their own ideas, and can say "I hear voices and I'm happy about it".

NB: The information in this section is taken from the results of questionnaires sent to voice hearers and from subsequent interviews (see *Accepting Voices* by Marius Romme and Sandra Escher)

If this is the case, it is no longer a sustainable position to think of voices as part of a disease syndrome, such as schizophrenia, instead hearing voices can be regarded as a meaningful, real (although sometimes painful, fearful and overwhelming) events, that speak to the person in a metaphorical way about their lives, emotions and environment. For instance, people experiencing distress as a consequence of abusive or commanding voices can often recognise their voices as those of their actual abusers and the voices have the effect of attacking their sense of self esteem and worth.

Having discovered these kinds of relationships, voice hearers, nurses, psychiatrists and psychologists throughout the world are developing techniques to assist voice hearers focus on their experience and get to know their voices better. The new approach requires the voice hearer to make space for the voices, to listen but not to necessarily follow, to engage, but in your own time and space – essentially to learn how to control them in your own terms, according to your own beliefs and explanatory framework. This acceptance of the voices is crucial to growth and resolution, voice hearers who have learnt these techniques can now say "I hear voices, they are part of me and I am glad they are".

How to zap voices you don't like

So, what do you do about voices that are not on your side, which denigrate you and insult you, or interrupt your thoughts, or pander detrimental advice and tell you to do stupid things? The first thing to realise is that although the voice may be intruding on your consciousness, that does not mean that you should blindly do what it says. Would you rush off and commit murder if someone told you to? Absolutely not. People who hear voices have the same right to self-determination as anyone else and you can tell the voices exactly that. If some of the voices are pleasant and friendly, then clearly you chat to them, and not to the ones who are not. You can tell the unpleasant voices that you find them neither pleasant nor useful, and that you have no reason to tolerate them unless they are both.

What about malevolent voices who can cause acute mental pain and can order you to do things (like staying in and avoiding people)? One solution is to remove as much stress from your life as possible. Not only does stress increase the voices, but it makes them say more unpleasant things. Secondly, do not ignore the voices as they tend to get more aggressive, however at the same time do not let them get away with running your life without your permission.

Gaining power over your voices

It is very important to recognise that the voices know the person who hears them very well, that they always say things that are especially relevant to them and that are related to their problems. The voices usually refer to unsolved problems in daily life and/or emotions related to a trauma that has not yet been resolved, or to unrealised hopes and aspirations that, in some cases, are impossible to realise. Therefore in working with a voice hearer it is not valid to reject the voices', instead, it is more appropriate to stimulate the curiosity of the voice hearer about what the voices are saying. As long as the voice hearer is only able to react to the voices in an emotional way, they dis-empower them and it is therefore difficult to stimulate their curiosity. This process is difficult to accomplish and we have been exploring techniques that appeal to people hearing voices.

This exploration is being conducted in cooperation with people hearing voices and as a result the following constructive techniques used by people hearing voices to improve their coping skills have been identified:

Table VIII: Strategies for Coping with Distressing Voices

HVN Australia have put together this list of ways that people who hear voices have said have helped them cope with their voices:

FOCUSING TECHNIQUES
• Accepting that voices are not 'the' problem, they are a consequence of a problem. Your job is to find out more
• Identify your voices— number, gender, age and so on
• Learn about boundaries to apply to people and your voices (i.e., make a deal with your voices, "be quiet now and I'll listen later")
• Listen out for positive voices too—they can be allies
• Schedule a time to listen to the voices and ask them to leave you alone until that time
• Tell negative voices that you will only talk with them if they are respectful towards you
• Voice dialogue— let a trusted family member, friend or mental health worker talk directly to your voices
• Work through Ron Coleman & Mike Smith's "Working with Voices

---

II" work book (see further reading) with a trusted family member, friend or mental health worker
• Write down what the voices are saying to you

POSITIVE EMOTIONAL TECHNIQUES
• Go for a picnic
• Listen to energetic music
• Look at good things achieved list
• Look at photo albums
• Look at the list of good things others have said about you
• Make a list of your assets or strengths
• Make an emergency comfort bundle (of goodies)
• Read books, love letters, love poems
• Read joke books / emails
• Say positive statements to self
• Record positive statements on tape (your voice)
• Watch films – comedy or inspirational

POINTS TO REMEMBER TO ENABLE ME TO LOOK AFTER MYSELF:
• Do something nice for 'me' each day
• Eat a healthy diet
• Keep regular appointments with my support network even if I am feeling OKAY
• Look up, get perspective, stretch or shift your body
Try to see the grey areas
• Plan my day; ensure I do not have long periods
of time with nothing to do
• Reach out. Talk to someone
• Take medication as prescribed (in consultation)
• Think about how I am feeling and be realistic about what I can achieve

EMOTIONAL FOCUSING
• Discuss feelings with another person
• List emotional triggers
• Paint / draw emotions

- Rainy day letter
- Write a diary
- Write poetry / prose regarding feelings

THINGS THAT MAY HELP VOICE HEARERS TO COPE
- Acupuncture
- Avoiding street drugs
- Chanting or singing
- Distraction e.g. reading, and computer games
- Focusing on the voices
- Going to Hearing Voices Groups
- Having good support around you, good friends, family, nurse, counsellor etc.
- Holidays
- Humour
- Identifying when you are most likely to hear the voices
- Ignoring voices
- Isolating self
- Keeping a diary about them
- Keeping occupied e.g. cooking, house chores
- Keeping physically active and healthy
- Listening to music
- Massage
- Meditation
- Money
- Positive attitudes
- Praying /speaking to God
- Religion/Deliverance and Healing
- Sex
- Shouting at the voices
- Sleeping
- Staff listening to you
- Talking (to a trusted person)

WHAT MAY NOT HELP
- Being over-medicated
- Being told not to talk about voices

- Dreams and trying to get to sleep
- Labelling
- Lack of sleep
- Not having information
- Other people denying the existence of voices
- Other people denying your explanation of your voices
- Professionals thinking they know more about your voices than you do
- Side effects of the medication
- Thinking negatively
- Being socially isolated

RELAXATION TECHNIQUES
- Acknowledge fear, worry, and stress and let go consciously. Trust
- Count your breaths
- Dancing / walking
- Focus on the position of your body
- Focus solely on breathing / breathe deeply
- Give yourself permission to relax
- Guided fantasy dream time
- Learn (figure 8) Yoga breath
- Listen to guided relaxation on tape
- Listen to relaxing music
- Massage hands, feet, head, etc.
- Relax each muscle individually
- Swimming / floating
- Yoga

THINGS THAT MAY WORK FOR ME IN A CRISIS
- Ask for help sooner not later
- Create a personalised crises plan when you are feeling well
- Cry
- Find a safe place
- Hand in my medication / blades or other similar items
- Have PRN medication
- Kick boxes around outside
- Let people know where I am

- Let someone know how I am feeling
- Plan safety
- Remember that situations and feelings frequently change –"This too shall pass" (King Solomon)
- Rest on my bed
- Shout into my pillow
- Try to identify how I am feeling

COMFORTING TECHNIQUES
- Buy / pick fresh flowers
- Change the sheets on your bed
- Cuddle up to a teddy
- Eat a favourite food in moderation
- Have a bubble bath
- Have a soothing drink
- Hold a safe comforting object
- Find a safe space
- Hug someone
- Listen to soothing music / favourite soft music
- Prayer / meditation /creative visualization
- Put lights / radio on (to sleep)
- Sing favourite songs
- Sit in a safe place
- Soak your feet / Radox bath
- Spray room fragrance
- Stroke / brush your pet or someone else's
- Use perfume / hand cream or take a warm bath
- Use pot pourri / essential oils
- Wear comfortable clothes
- Write a diary or talk about how you feel with another person
- Zen seeing (with a friend)

GENERAL IDEAS
- Don't beat yourself up, we all make mistakes
- List achievements
- Make a contract with your voices
- Positive self talk

- Self forgiveness (find yourself innocent)
- Talk to the voices, find out how they feel
- Wear one ear plug

DISTRACTION TECHNIQUES*
- Cinema
- Clean or tidy things up
- Do puzzles or develop a hobby
- Exercise – walking/running/dance/beach
- Gardening / striking pot plants
- Listening to CDs / mp3 player
- Paint or draw pictures /posters / cards
- Playing games/cards/computer
- Reading out aloud or hum a tune to yourself
- Sewing / knitting / collecting
- Shopping
- Sports
- Telephone a friend
- Use visual imagery or count to yourself when trying to get to sleep
- Visit a friend
- Walk in shallow water
- Washing
- Watch TV / video
- Write letters

*NOTE: Distraction techniques are useful when voices are particularly distressing or intrusive but are not recommended as an on-going coping technique

Making Sense of voices

Making Sense of voices is a method to explore the problems in the life of the voice hearer that lie at the roots of the hearing voices experience developed by Marius Romme and Sandra Escher. In this section we take a closer look at this approach and how they developed it.

Over the years Marius and Sandra came across people who heard voices and had never been psychiatric patients. They were and are functioning quite well socially. This was a shocking experience for Marius, because as a psychiatrist he had always identified hearing voices with psychopathology. From the meetings he held between voice hearers and from their study comparing patients with non-patients, it became clear that there was a relationship between hearing voices and life events that make people feel powerless.

As a result of their study of the experiences of voice hearers it became clear that hearing voices in itself is not a symptom of an illness: Most people who hear voices (including those using psychiatric services and those outside of psychiatry) do so as a reaction to severe traumatic experiences that made the person powerless, therefore the voices can be thought of as a kind of survival strategy.

So they argued, if hearing voices in itself is not a sign of illness but a signal that there are problems often emotionally overwhelming problems – then these are the problems that need to be solved or coped with. For instance they noted that it is mostly accepted that when people suffer from mental health problems like: depression, anxiety, phobias, dissociative disorders eating disorders etc. they do so in reaction to daily life problems. This mostly involves difficulties and traumas in peoples relationship with significant others – or in relation to social structures and rules that troubles them greatly. As they are not able to cope with these situations they can develop mental health problems which are an expression of these serious difficulties. The same goes for voices.

Furthermore, healthy people hearing voices make up about 4 to 6% of the population, whilst for in-patient groups –

such as people diagnosed with schizophrenia and dissociative disorder and affective disorder – the percentage of people hearing voices is much higher: 30-50%. This seemed to be discrepancy and led them to take an interest in the life history of voice hearers. Because they came from a social psychiatric background, Marius and Sandra had an appreciation that patients might have experienced more problems in their life histories than non-patients and that they might not have been able to solve these problems. Therefore they held extensive interviews with the voice hearers in three research groups, patients diagnosed with schizophrenia, patients diagnosed with dissociative disorder and non-patients and they found the following relationships between hearing voices and the life history of the voice hearer:

• There is a significant relationship between the onset of the voices and intense difficulty or traumatic experience. This occurs in 70 to 80% of the patients and in 50% of the non-patients hearing voices.
• Voices can function as a defence mechanism against overwhelming emotions. This is an indication that the person has special difficulty with expressing emotions. For example, if the voice makes the person angry or an anger provoking situation is a trigger, the person presumably has a serious difficulty in expressing anger and therefore expressing anger is something that has to be learned (this however is not as easy as it sounds).
• Voices express themselves in a metaphoric way. This can be useful in detecting problems related to the persons' circumstances that they have to deal with. For example, if voices mix up numbers in the head of the voice hearer when studying, this often, but not always, means the area

of study or the class level or the course is too difficult for the person to cope with.

• The relationship with hearing voices and traumatic experiences occurs in about 70 to 80% of cases. Mostly voice hearers who become patients have suffered extreme traumatic experiences like physical and/or sexual abuse as a child or as an adult. Also quite a lot of people have insoluble problems relating to their sexual identity; problems of very unfair treatment at work; or losing a loved one in complicated circumstances.

They concluded that when hearing voices in itself is not a sign of mental illness but the difficulty to cope with these voices seems to be the problem, then the person should be helped to cope with the voices. And when the voices are a signal that there are serious problems the person has not solved, or learned to cope with, those problems should be worked through.

Marius and Sandra concluded that ways of helping voice hearers should be focussed on the needs of the person instead of on the theoretical concepts of the professionals.

Table IX: Why hearing voices in itself is not a symptom of illness

Four reasons why hearing voices (aka auditory hallucinations) are not in in themselves a sign of mental illness, but rather a signal of a problem with living your life:

Research has clearly shown that hearing voices is also apparent in healthy people who never become psychiatric patients.

The reason for becoming a psychiatric patient is not the voices themselves, but rather not being able to cope with the voices, nor with the problems that lie at their roots. In our society there are more people who hear voices and do not become patients than there are persons who hear voices and become patients.

Hearing voices is a very personal experience related to very personal problems often related to social situations and interactions that make a person powerless.

Compare voices with messengers that bring sometimes-awful messages and are then seen as the ones that brings the evil. People then fight the messenger because they are not able to accept the message.

PART 4: HELPING PEOPLE WHO HEAR VOICES
THAT CAUSE PROBLEMS

What Marius Romme says

Romme's research has come up with a very different answer than the traditional psychiatric view described above. The reason for this, is that Marius developed his understanding of the voice hearing experience by talking to voice hearers themselves and asking them the basic and obvious questions such as:

> *When did the voices start?*
> *How many voices do you hear?*
> *How often do you hear them?*
> *What do you think the voice represents?*
> *What do they say?*
> *What helps?*

As I pointed out earlier these questions had never been asked before in a systematic way and the direct subjective experience of the voice hearer had been largely ignored. Romme came to the conclusion that to regard hearing voices as part of an illness and to ignore the content of the voice hearing experience is largely unhelpful and counter productive – in that ignoring the voices (and long term use of psychiatric drugs) can make the voices worse. It may also be an inaccurate analysis, for outside the world of psychiatry, there are many people who hear voices and manage to live with the experience. Marius concludes that it is not the fact that you hear voices that is the problem, it is the way you deal with them – and further that psychosis, like neurosis, is firmly related to an individual's life history.

Hearing voices: Don't kill the messenger

"They are messengers and they have a message. They are related to sincere problems that occurred in the person's life and they tell us about those problems. Therefore it is not wise to kill the messenger. Instead of not-listening to the message we should be considering how to help and sustain the person in solving their problems. (Otherwise it is like behaving as it has been the case in wars and conflicts in ancient times, where the messengers were killed when the message was not welcome).

Research shows also that hearing voices in itself is not related to the illness of schizophrenia. In population research only 16% of the whole group of voice hearers can be diagnosed with schizophrenia.

Also, therefore, it is not right to identify hearing voices as an illness. Psychiatry in our western culture, however, tends unjustly to identify hearing voices with schizophrenia. Going to a psychiatrist with hearing voices gives you an 80% chance of getting a diagnosis of schizophrenia.

However, when you identify hearing voices with illness and try to kill the voices with neuroleptic medication, you just miss the personal problems that lay at the roots of hearing voices – and you will not help the person solving those problems. You just make a chronic patient."

Marius Romme 2000

75

Table X: An exercise in how to replicate the experience of hearing voices

The following exercise was developed by my friend, Ron Coleman, as a way to simulate what it is like to hear voices and was developed to try to give mental health workers and relatives some insight into what it is like to hear intrusive, negative and commanding voices. Ron was a voice hearer for many years and is now a trainer and consultant.

1. Form a group of three people, the first person takes the part of the "voice", the second as the voice hearer, the third a person with whom the voice hearer is conducting a "real" conversation. The "voice" positions him or herself close to one the ears of the voice hearer whilst the other two face each other seated on chairs. There can be a number of threesomes carrying out this exercise at the same time

2. For two minutes the "voice" talks to the voice hearer whilst at the same time the voice hearer conducts a conversation with the the third person. The "voice" is instructed to make personal and belittling remarks to the hearer in a clear voice and to try to engage the attention of the voice hearer. At the end of two minutes the three switch roles until everyone has experienced being a voice hearer.

3. At the end of the exercise the threesomes are brought together and are asked to describe what it felt like to hear voices (i.e. confusion, frustration, annoyance, anger, depression, weariness) how it effected their ability to hold a conversation (i.e. loss of attention and concentration) what strategies they employed to reduce the intrusion of the voice (i.e. trying to ignore it, answering back, changing physical position). Other questions include asking what they would feel and do if the voice was permanent? (depression, suicidal feelings, a desire to avoid people, to hide away, to talk to the voice more). Conversely also ask what they

thought about trying to conduct a conversation with someone
who is hearing a voice (and being a voice!).

4. List all the points raised by the participants and then compare
them with those described in the three three phases of voice
hearing , it is often the case that non voice hearers list exactly
the same symptoms and ways of trying to respond.

Implications for Friends and relatives and people who hear voices[36]

These are some of the reactions that friends and relatives
have experienced when someone close to them started
hearing voices:
- knowing something was not quite right
- feeling in an awful position and not knowing who
to turn to.
- feeling helpless and not knowing how to offer help.
- finding yourself looking at your loved one and
thinking "they have changed, I don´t   understand   them
any more, who are they?".
- Worrying about what people might think and being
afraid of the stigma associated with being a friend or family
member of some one who hears voices
- not wanting your relative or friend to be labelled.
- finding people think that the person's parents are
responsible or to blame.

---

36. Sources: Dundee Hearing Voices Network, *A simple guide
for relatives and friends* – and – Newcastle, North Tyneside and
Northumberland Mental Health NHS Trust, *Understanding Voices
and Disturbing Beliefs: A self-help guide* (2002)

Things that you can do that will help you and the person who hears voices:

• Accept that the voices exist and that they area real experience for the person hearing them

• Offer good listening (stay open minded, ask open questions, sound encouraging and try not to interpret or interrupt) as this will allow the person to express their feelings and explanation for what they think is happening to them.

• Do not deny that the experience is happening or contradict, just note what they say and ask follow up questions that might reveal more about the experience.

• Tackle any problems that may arise form the experience as calmly and objectively as you can

• Look after yourself, this is very important, for instance give yourself some time and space to relax.

• Living with someone who hears voices can be a very intense and baffling experience, it is OK to take some time out if you feel you need to. Check out to see if any support is available to you from local carer groups, including meeting with other carers, these contact can be crucial in helping you breakdown your sense of isolation. If you need to seek professional help

• Learn to say "no" when you think it is necessary, for instance on setting limits on difficult behaviour

Helping to empower the person who hears voices:

• Help them to try and think and plan for what they want in the future
• Help them regain a sense of being in charge of their life

- Find out if there is a hearing voices self help group and see if they want to go along
- Try to avoid being critical
- Try to offer the person who hears voices warmth and support

Implications for mental health workers

We would very much like to encourage people working in the mental health professions to examine in greater detail which frames of reference and coping strategies seem to be the most useful to their patients who hear voices; by doing so, we believe you will be able to support and assist voice hearers much more effectively in their attempts to deal with their experiences. Here are some ways you could help:

• Accept the voice hearer's experience of the voices. The voices are often felt as more intense and real than sensory perceptions.

• Try to understand the different languages used by the voice hearer to describe and account for their experiences, as well as the language spoken by the voices themselves. There is often a world of symbols and feelings involved; for example, a voice might speak of light and dark when expressing love and aggression. Consider helping the individual to communicate with the voices. This may involve issues of differentiating between good and bad voices and of accepting the voice hearer's own negative emotions. This kind of acceptance may make a crucial contribution to the promotion of self-esteem.

• Encourage the voice hearer to meet other people with similar experiences and to read about hearing voices, in order to help overcome isolation and taboo.

- Normalise the experience through an educational approach to reduce anxiety and by giving people information and training on more effective ways of coping with the voices then the ones they may be using.

- Focus on the voices by examining the characteristics of the voices and the relationship of the voices with the person who hears them.

- Re-author life. Help the voice hearer to take ownership of the experience by writing their own life story especially in relationship to the voices. The From Victim to Victor workbook is a good example of this approach.

- Seeking active solutions for the social and emotional problems that are at the root of many voice-hearing experiences. Seeking not only to influence the methods used in coping with voices, but also to change the manner in which the person copes with their daily life problems and emotions.

- Influencing beliefs. This technique encourages voice-hearers to check out their belief system about the meaning of the voices and to decide for themselves the validity of the meaning. This is a way of moving away from the 'my belief/your delusion' dispute into an open dialogue about the origin and purpose of the voices.

Peer support and self help groups

Self help groups have been one of the most successful ways to open up discussion about hearing voices. A safe place to talk about voices is important in a society that stigmatises the experience and has resulted in many voice hearers have keeping silent about what they are experiencing. Self help groups can reduce the isolation that people feel and it can be very helpful to talk to other people who share your experience. In England there are over 180 self help groups where voice hearers meet regularly to share their experiences and to learn more about how to cope with their voices.

The self-help group was first established in Manchester with the simple idea that bringing together people with a common experience might be helpful .

Why set up self-help groups?

One of the problems that is common to all voice hearers and stands in the way of coping successfully with hearing voices is the effects of the taboo that prevent the experience being discussed openly in he same way that one would discuss hearing from an old friend or discuss a recently read book. It is not possible to change social attitudes overnight.

It is, however, possible for people who hear voices and who recognise that they have a need to accept the voices as part of their lives, or have a wish to accept responsibility for their own mental health, or, who believe that as patients in a psychiatric system, their right to have a treatment that addresses the real symptoms is not being met, to form self help and support groups.

Why attend a self-help group?

For many people, attending a hearing voices self help group is the first time they have had the opportunity to talk freely about their voices with other voice hearers and the first time that their voice hearing experience has been seen as something real and not necessarily negative, and consequently can be a very large step in beginning to cope or learning to cope better.

Voice hearers often feel isolated and a self help

group offers them a place to release themselves from the repressive energy of having to keep quiet about the voices and trying to keep the voices quiet and controlled in a world where their existence is largely denied. The groups also offer regular opportunities for conversation and exchange of experiences and ideas with people who have an intrinsic understanding of the experience. The sharing of experiences, gives the voice hearer the opportunity to be more honest to them whilst feeling supported and bonded to a group whose strength is as a result of the common experience of hearing voices. This can give room for growth in the individuals as a result of the accepting and non judgemental atmosphere of the group after years of repression. When this is coupled with the positive reinforcement that people experience, when they find that there is a wide diversity of experiences in a group, it gives them extra confidence to live their lives.

The group meetings are also an opportunity for shared jokes that voice hearers understand and they are a social engagement for some people where it is possible for isolated voice hearers to gain confidence in socialising and, as a result of being valued by the group, (for the experiences that they have had and for the support that they give to other members) can feel a sense of increasing self confident and self esteem.

What Self help groups can offer and what they do

Attending a hearing voices self help group gives voice hearers the opportunity to gain knowledge from other voice hearers. It can also further increase their idea of self worth, gained from a feeling of belonging to the group that gives the voice hearer some social status as a result of the experience of hearing voices that society denies them.

The group, however, should be as outwardly looking as possible, always remaining a means to an end rather than an end in itself. This is to ensure that the group does not dominate the life of the voice hearers, rather that it continues as a constantly changing group and not with a short-sighted vision to build voice-hearing ghettos. In order to bring about social change voice hearers should be able to talk freely in their homes, in their workplaces and in their colleges and universities so that they may lead a whole and satisfying life and the voices may be incorporated into that life. The self-help groups can help them to gain the confidence and skills to do this. Ideally the content of the discussion should include time spent in discussing the coping with the reluctance of others to accept the changes that occur in the voice hearer as a result of attending the group.

Self-help groups can be criticised for being an inferior form of therapy. Hearing voices self help groups, however, are not therapy groups. They are formed in a response to a need. That need is a safe place where voice hearers can talk freely and so reduce the burden of the stigma of hearing voices and consequently grow with equal opportunities as those who don't hear voices.

Some self help groups are just for voice hearers whilst other groups allow people who do not hear voices are to attend. They may be support workers, without whom a voice hearer could not attend, or social workers who would like to learn more about the voice hearing experience and voice hearer's approaches to coping.

How self help groups can be run

In some ways it is contradictory to have group leaders in a self help group, but, from our experience we have seen that the stability of the group is important and with a membership that fluctuates from meeting to meeting it is helpful to have a key member or members who take responsibility for the practicalities of the room and refreshments and also for maintaining the cohesion and direction of the group and to make sure that everyone has an equal chance to participate in the discussion and to notice when other group members are dominating the discussion.

One important role is that of discussion leader, this role can be rotated amongst established members or be held by one person. Amongst the qualities that a discussion leader must possess is integrity in their intentions in the position of discussion leader. It is important in order to maintain an atmosphere of trust, security and sharing, for new members to trust the discussion leaders and for other existing members to build and reinforce their confidence and trust in the group.

Discussion leaders should also have a positive and possibly active approach to health and to not only maintain an atmosphere of well being, but also to be able to maintain discussion on different approaches to health and to encourage, and maintain that encouragement, with anyone who is working towards a healthier lifestyle.

The discussion leaders should also be non judgemental and open to the ideas about voices and coping techniques that the group members have, within the confines of what the group see to be acceptable. They must also value personal change and growth in order to keep the group as a space for change and growth and to help reduce the blocks that result from the stigma of hearing voices and deprive voice hearers of the freedom to change easily.

Not all group members will automatically be able to cope within a group, so, once again it is useful to have a key person who new members can look to until they settle into the group and develop their self confidence in how to exchange ideas, vocalise their thoughts, and how to give and receive support and encouragement whilst at the same time enjoying the group meeting.

Voice hearer only groups

The development of the these kinds of groups are intended to give voice hearers the opportunity to develop skills in participating in a group and also receive more individual assistance in developing ideas and coping techniques. These groups are open to voice hearers only, giving the voice hearer the maximum opportunity to unlock him or herself from the well-intentioned caring of non-voice hearers, particularly families or spouses.

Table XI: Talk about it: a hearing voices check list

Talking about voices can really help. The following key points provide a useful guide to opening up discussion about the voice hearing experience.

1. Open discussion: People who hear voices find themselves having to deal with an other world that may overwhelm them and claim their attention to the exclusion of all else. As a result the power of reason may be virtually extinguished, at least initially, making it impossible for those concerned to go about their daily lives without being affected by such a penetrating and confusing experience.

Open discussion with others offers the most important means of creating some kind of order in the attempt to come to terms with these experiences. In particular, communication helps people to accept their voices; as a result self-confidence is improved, freeing them from isolation and reaffirming their sense of involvement with those around them. Mutual communication between voice hearers gives the opportunity to share similar experiences, using a common language and to learn from one another.

2. Recognising patterns: People who hear voices say it is very important to discuss voices in the same way one might talk about disagreeable relatives. In the process, it is possible to learn to recognise their games and tricks, as well as their more pleasant aspects, and to identify patterns that are specific to given situations. Such knowledge can help the voice hearer to be better prepared for any subsequent onset of the voices.

3. Easing anxiety: Most people who hear voices initially imagine that they are alone in doing so. This can make the experience anxious and unpleasant and also produces feelings of shame or the fear of going mad. Anxiety often leads to the avoidance of situations which might trigger the hearing of voices, and this avoidance seriously blocks self-development. Thus some voice hearers cannot go to the supermarket or socialise at parties. Such levels of anxiety severely restrict freedom of movement, and strategies of avoidance often seem only to exacerbate the problem.

4. Finding a theoretical perspective: Like professionals in the field, voice hearers themselves look for a theoretical explanation to account for the existence of their voices. A personal approach to understanding or a specific frame of reference can be helpful and there are many disparate perspectives used by voice hearers. These include psycho dynamic, mystical, parapsychology and medical models. Whatever the perspective adopted, some kind of explanatory theory does appear to be essential to the development of a coping strategy. Unless some meaning is attributed to the voices, it is very difficult to begin to organise one's relationship with them in order to reduce anxiety. Generally speaking, perspectives that discourage the individual from seeking mastery of the voices

tend to yield the least positive results. Interpreting ones voices as the manifestation of electronic influences might be one such example. The explanation offered by biological psychiatry may also be unhelpful in terms of coping strategies, given that, it too, places the phenomenon beyond one's personal grasp.

5. Acceptance: In the process of developing one's own point of view and taking responsibility for oneself, the essential first step is acceptance of the voices as belonging to me. This is of the utmost importance – and also one of the most difficult steps to take.

6. Recognising meaning: Voices can express what the voice hearer is feeling or thinking, for instance aggression or fear about an event or a relationship. When voices offer information in this way the challenge posed by their presence is often less significant than the reason for the anger or fear. When the voices express such views and feeling it can be valuable to discuss the nature of the messages.

7. Positive aspects: When people hear voices that are truly malicious – ridiculing or belittling others, or even abusing the hearers until they are driven to injure themselves – it may be difficult to persuade them to accept the existence of a positive, helpful dimension to the experience. Contact with others can lead to the surprising discovery that positive voices do exist, and to the realisation that these may arise, or be detected, as a result of a proper acceptance of the hearer's own negative side.

8. Structuring contact: Imposing a structure on the relationship with the voices can help minimise the common feelings of powerlessness. It can be extremely valuable in helping people to see that they can set their own limits and restrain the voices from excessive intrusion.

9. More effective use of medication: Sharing experiences also enables people to get to know what medicines others are using, how useful these are, and what their side effects may be. It is important, for example, to know whether a particular medicine has been found helpful in reducing the hearing of voices or in easing the associated anxiety and confusion.

10. Family understanding: Sharing knowledge about voice hearing with families and friends can be very helpful. If a person's family

and friends can accept the voices they can be more supportive, this can make the life of the voice hearer easier, improving their sense of confidence in social situations.

11. Personal Growth: Almost all voice hearers who have learned to adjust to their experiences report that, with hindsight, the process has contributed to their personal growth. Personal growth can be defined as recognising what one needs in order to live a fulfilled life, and knowing how to achieve these ends; it could be described as a process of emancipation.

12. Watch out: Communicating about voices does have its disadvantages, exposing oneself can make one feel very vulnerable. Some voice hearers find great difficulty in opening up about their experiences, though it can be easier with other voice hearers. In particular, voice hearers who have never been psychiatric patients need real courage to face a world that will all too often call them mad when they talk about their lives. It can be hard to see what would be gained by doing so, and often their only motive is to help others who are unable to cope with their own voices. Another possible drawback to disclosures is that the voices may occasionally become temporarily more acute. All in all, though, the advantages definitely outweigh the disadvantages. Finally, one must always be wary of advice and explanations that are purely personal convictions and make no allowance for any other interpretation. It is most important to be fully aware of the wide variety of individual situations and circumstances. The least hazardous advice tends to be that which may serve to increase the individual's own influence over their voices, rather than intensify powerlessness.

Self determination and self knowledge are the key words

Talking to and with Challenging Voices

Over the years we have noticed that many people who hear challenging voices told us they have found that a turning point in learning to cope had been finding different ways of talking with and understanding their voices. We discovered that learning to understand the motives of the voices and different ways of talking with them can help the relationship to change between the voice hearer and the voices.

Over the last ten years, a growing number of individuals including Marius Romme and Ron Coleman and especially the psychiatrist, Dirk Corstens, and two voice hearers and psychologists, Eleanor Longden and Rufus May have followed up this approach. They have adapted techniques from various psychological and dramatic traditions (e.g. Gestalt, Voice Dialogue, Transactional Analysis, Psychodrama) to use with voice-hearing, they call this approach "voice dialogue". To give an example, one way they encourage people to communicate with their voices is to set out chairs for the voices and to to act out the different roles and relationships they have with their voices.

The basic principle behind this approach is not to try to change the voices; instead they try to explore the relationship the voices have with the person. The objective of this approach is to help the individual gain a different perspective on what the voices are trying to say. If the voice hearer can develop a a more positive and stronger attitude then the voices are able to change. The aim is not to get rid of the voices but instead to help the person take back more control in the relationship they have with the voices.

They point out because many voice hearers experience their voices as powerful, and it seems to them they have to obey to everything they say and that the voices tell the ultimate truth. Voices can also threaten voice hearers with "punishments" directed at them or people close to them. With this approach the goal is to explore the motives of the voices so that the voice hearer can find new strategies to cope with their voices. When is is successful it can create more autonomy and independence for the voice hearer so that they can make more easily their own own choices. Some people even find that their voices can become supportive.

Why is Voice Dialogue appropriate for voice hearers?

It is not oriented towards pathology nor is it focused upon discovering what is wrong. It offers a neutral but strong attitude to work with voices – acceptance is the core of the work.

It offers a "positive" model for the existence of voices.

It helps to built up more awareness – some distance towards the voices – and a more fruitful relationship between voices and voice hearer.

The results of this work has shown that this approach can be very helpful in order to help people resolve conflicts and reclaim power in their lives.

Table XII
Excerpt from article by Adam James, PsychMinded, February 13, 2009

New dialogues on voices:

Voice hearers are in a perpetual relationship with their voices, often continually conversing with them. A third person relating directly to the voice can bring benefits. Dr May says: "For many people the most troubling thing is for the hearer to be alone with their voice. With someone else hearing what the voice says it means the voice is being witnessed [by someone else] – this can be validating and assuring. While some cognitive approaches might mindfully step back from the voices, voice dialogue can be seen as mindfully engaging with voices. But I'll only talk to the voice if it actually helps the person, and voice dialogue is only one of many ways I might try and help someone."

Dr Dirk Corstens, a psychiatrist and psychotherapist from Maastricht, Holland, who for 10 years has been running voice dialogue workshops for UK mental health professionals says: "Instead of using role play I talk to the voices. Often a person will talk all day to their voices. Voices can give important information about a person's life."

… As importantly, adds Dr May, who was himself diagnosed with schizophrenia when aged 18, voice dialogue is supported by many in the service user movement. Plus, it provides carers, relatives, friends and users with a jargon-free method to help people.

"A caring relative or friend can use voice dialogue with a couple of days training," says Dr May. "Unlike CBT, it's not stipulated that voice dialogue is only for professionals. You do not need a degree or diploma. It's not a therapy, as such. It's a way to help people deal with their voices. I'm interested in how knowledge in mental health can be redistributed, rather than being something only professionals have."

PART 5: THE FUTURE?

Hearing voices and the implications for schizophrenia

Many researchers and practitioners involved in the hearing voices movement have been considering what the research into hearing voices may mean for our understanding of schizophrenia. In fact it has led them to develop what Marius calls a "cause related alternative for the concept of schizophrenia". Increasing numbers of people involved in the hearing voice movement now think that there is strong case for considering schizophrenia as a harmful concept that needs to be abolished.

Here is a summary of Marius's views on schizophrenia:

Schizophrenia has yet to be shown to be a proven disease.

There is no physical, nor psychological test for schizophrenia and in all honesty psychiatry can only say that schizophrenia is a concept, a theory that has yet to be proved.

In spite of this psychiatry acts as if schizophrenia is a proven disease and the treatments offered and most of the information available to ordinary people about schizophrenia perpetuates this idea.

There are now well known reasons for why people suffer from the kind of complaints that make up schizophrenia, but the way schizophrenia is constructed obscures these reasons

An important development in psychiatry in psychiatry over the last 30 years is that it has reached the conclusion that social and emotional factors are not essential factors in the development of psychosis. Whilst psychiatry concedes that these factors may have a role as triggers they claim they are not part of the cause. These conclusions are claimed to be based on medically rigorous research and observations. But as Marius points out, this is not the way in general that medicine works. Ordinarily, you do not start with a disease and look for the reasons that may cause it, instead you do it the other way round and look for the reasons that lie behind the complaints and the discovery of these reasons are essential for the establishment of a diagnosis.

So, what exactly is the problem? Well, in clinical psychiatry a diagnosis in the area of psychosis[37](such as schizophrenia) is constructed only on the basis of the behaviour and experiences. The great problem here, is that the consequent treatment is also given without analysing the causes for this behaviour and therefore only the "constructs"(that is the behaviours and experiences) are treated and not the problems that lie at their roots. Marius believes this is more like the legal and judicial system, which judges the behaviour of transgressors and is far less concerned by the reasons that may lie behind the behaviour. Therefore it is not strange that many patients in psychiatric services are not very happy with this situation. They are quite right.

Whilst Marius accepts that suffering and serious complaints are sensibly seen as an illness experience, however, this does not conclusively mean that there the cause is a disease entity like the construct of schizophrenia. As these 'symptom' experiences do not result from an underlying disease, they are not really symptoms at all, and might well

37.. See The Campaign for the Abolition of the Schizophrenia Label (CASL) website at http://www.caslcampaign.com/

have another origin. Therefore the conclusion can well be that:

The people with the illness experiences exist but the disease 'schizophrenia' does not, and therefore in this sense the illness, does not exist.

Table XIII: The problem with schizophrenia:

- Schizophrenia is not a valid concept because it completely fails scientific tests
- Therefore schizophrenia is not and never has been proven to be a brain disease.
- The way in which people are diagnosed as having schizophrenia gives no consideration to the underlying reasons for the symptoms that people may be experiencing.
- The way in which people are diagnosed as having schizophrenia neglects the very real relationships between the core symptoms (such as voices) and the individuals past experiences in life.
- The relationships between the core symptoms are neglected, for instance the persons own explanations for their voices are not considered, neither are what the voices say, or why and when they arose.
- The core symptoms do not represent expressions of psychopathology.
- Learning to cope with the symptoms and with the problems at the heart of these symptoms are neglected by psychiatry.
- People can recover from schizophrenia and most people who do so, manage this outside of psychiatry.

If it is not schizophrenia what is it?

Even psychiatry acknowledges that there are no particular causes for schizophrenia (although they are still looking and have been doing so for over a hundred years now), however we now know that that there are causes for the different core symptoms of schizophrenia in individual cases. The diagnosis of schizophrenia is harmful because it mystifies the causes for the various behaviours and experiences of the individual, when in fact it is these very causes that need to be analysed and can become the successful focus of therapy.

What are these causes?

Marius's research concerning people who hear voices found that for 77% of the people diagnosed with schizophrenia the hearing of voices was related to traumatic experiences. These traumatic experiences varied from being sexually abused, physically abused, being extremely belittled over long periods from young age, being neglected during long periods as a youngster, being very aggressively treated in marriage, not being able to accept ones sexual identity, etc. Many people start to hear voices and only afterwards developed the other experiences. These arise as a reaction to hearing the voices and because people cannot cope with their voices. One of the clearest interrelationships that have been scientifically studied is the explanation people give for their voices. Because the voices are for the voice hearer a strange, unknown experience, the explanation they think of is also mostly strange for us and therefore easily identified as a delusion. This means that the auditory hallucinations and delusion are interrelated and not separate symptoms of an illness. This holds for many symptoms of schizophrenia, being secondary reactions to a primary symptom like hearing voices that scares the person and with which they are not able to cope.

When we look at the concept of schizophrenia in this way we find the symptoms are not the results of an illness entity, but the illness picture is composed of primary symptoms, that are a reaction to traumatic experiences that have led to a psychological vulnerability, which includes serious difficulties in coping with emotions. When we consider hearing voices as a way of coping with this psychological vulnerability, then secondary reactions arise because of the inability to cope with this primary symptom.

Psychiatry disregards trauma as a cause

However, this process of developing psychosis has been totally abandoned in the concept of schizophrenia as used in psychiatry. This is a serious oversight, for if they seriously considered the traumatic experiences they could then perhaps understand and discuss the emotional consequences and problems that people endure. By not doing so, psychiatry is abdicating its responsibility to help people to understand the relationship between their voices and their experiences, to support them in finding other ways in coping with their voices and with their emotions involved in their traumatic experiences. Marius believes that as long as we try to cure the alleged illness then we are doing nothing but effectively suppressing emotions and because of this the person is being denied the opportunity to learn to cope with them and are therefore dammed to become or remain a chronically ill patient. In this sense the psychiatric approach has become a self fulfilling prophecy.

A more helpful approach

There are a great number of epidemiological studies that show us that there are quite a lot of individuals hearing voices and delusions without any apparent sign of psychiatric illness. In fact there are more people hearing voices or experiencing delusions without illness then people with these experiences that become psychiatric patients.

For mental health professionals, this is something that has proved to be very difficult to accept. The simple reason being is that they don't meet these people as they do not need psychiatric care. Many even say they are happy with their voices and their ideas about them because they have been helped by them in their daily lives.

This reality, that there are quite a large number of people (about 4%) in the general population who hear voices and even more (about 8%) have peculiar personal convictions, often referred to as delusions, without being ill, compels us to realise that the experience of hearing voices or having delusions are not in themselves a sign of mental illness. This is quite an important fact in understanding psychiatric patients with these experiences, because it opens our eyes for the reasons why the person became ill. A person hearing voices becomes ill, not because he hears voices but because he cannot cope with these voices and that again can be understood. Those who cannot cope with their voices cannot cope with them, because they cannot cope with the problems that led to the onset of the experience of hearing voices.

This double inability makes it important not to focus on an unknown disease but: To help the person to learn to accept and cope with his voices and or delusions and with the problems that led to them.

In this way it becomes clear that the focus on schizophrenia, an illness that does not even exist can not solve the problems that lie at the roots of becoming ill.

Whilst diagnosis and treatment remain focused on the

illness concept schizophrenia we will never be able to help people experiencing symptoms to solve their problems. In order to really help people we will first have to help them to cope with their experiences such as hearing voices or their personal convictions and that is by reducing the anxiety that arises from these experiences by using techniques such as cognitive interventions, which have been proven to be successful.

However, following these kinds of anxiety reduction techniques it is still necessary to help the person to learn to cope with the original problems that led to their mental health problems. This mostly concerns a change in attitude towards these problems and those people involved with them. This is not simple but is rewarding.

There is much more hope for recovery then you might think There can sometimes be a positive outcome with being angry with psychiatry. In the Hearing Voices Movement there are a number of people whose anger at the system and the medication was the beginning of their recovery journey.

This anger seemed to motivate people to try to take their lives in their own hands again or look elsewhere for help that had proved to be more successful. The catch 22 of course is that in mental health care, anger is often seen as part of the illness. Although anger is not a symptom of schizophrenia, it is instead interpreted as a lack of insight into the illness, which is a very dis-empowering interpretation.

On the other hand, the Hearing Voices Movement has seen that those who adapt to the psychiatric care system and the labels provided, seem less able to recover than people who protest against their diagnosis and treatment and also plan their own ways. From these experiences we should learn in mental health care. These experiences are well described by a number of well known psychiatric survivors like Peter Bullimore, Ron Coleman, Jacqui Dillon, Rufus May, Louise Pembroke and many others in the UK and elsewhere in the world.

Conclusions:

Schizophrenia as an illness entity does not exist

The Schizophrenia Concept is harmful because: It mystifies your social and emotional problems and it makes it impossible for you to solve your problems.

A diagnosis of "Trauma Induced Psychosis" should be recognised, as well as other cause related alternatives, like drug induced psychosis, identity induced psychosis etc.

Mental Health care should be oriented towards: Learning to cope with instead of the suppression of experiences; Analysing the causes of and learning to cope with emotions; Working toward recovery and the development of the person.

What Next?

Challenging traditional medical views about Hearing Voices

Why should you listen to this advice about voices, especially as this view of voices is not always shared by psychiatry?

For three reasons:

Firstly the advice has been developed from twenty years worth of research into the experience of voice hearers by psychiatrists and psychologists in the UK and the Netherlands and, most significantly, the lessons learnt have been consumer tested by voice hearers.

Secondly, hearing voices has been regarded by clinical psychiatry as an auditory hallucination and as a symptom of conditions such as schizophrenic disorders, bipolar disorder (manic depression) and psychosis. The usual treatment – major tranquillisers – are administered in order to reduce the delusions and hallucinations. However, not everyone responds to this type of treatment.

Thirdly, there are many people in the UK who hear voices, some of whom cope with their voices well without psychiatric intervention. This fact has been neglected. This guide shows there is another way of thinking about voices.

How you can recover

It is easy to underestimate the great difficulty people find in talking about the original problem that led to the voices and other experiences. It can be because of shame, because of guilt feelings, because of anxiety. In many ways, the same process are at work as with traumatic stress disorder.

People are brainwashed during their, often, long periods of traumatisation. They are reduced to nothing, made very afraid, made dependant, are heavily punished when expressing their emotions, are blackmailed. So they really have to work hard to try and tell their story and have to be helped with that in a safe supporting relationship. Another factor of difficulty is the anxiety that telling their story may lead to the voices being more aggressive or that the flash backs of horrible pictures will become more severe. These can be experienced as very overwhelming and intrusive, sometimes akin to the the feeling of being sexually overwhelmed and raped. We do not necessarily expect that you will be able to change the system and neither do we think that you will necessarily start a collective protest against the concept of schizophrenia because of the harm it causes.

However you are not powerless, for instance you can:

Use your own experiences, your own contacts with psychiatric services, with mental health workers you trust and with other patients experiencing psychosis to start talking about and listening to other peoples' psychotic experiences.

Consider further what it is you are experiencing and ask other people explain what they are experiencing.

You also consider what happened in your past life and ask what has happened to other people that may have led to experiencing psychosis.

Then differentiate for yourself and with other people the kinds of experiences like hearing voices, ideas of reference, delusions, the expressions of your negative symptoms (like lacking initiative, isolating yourself etc.).

You then can ask yourself; "What is the difficulty in coping with these experiences?" This will help you better understand the nature of your anxieties, depression, feelings of powerless etc.

You then can discuss how these experiences have developed over time and how they possibly interrelate with each other.

Groups

In these groups of voice hearers people can learn form each-other about coping with their voices and they can support each other in their battle to stop being discriminated against. Marius does not deny that there exists a pattern of behaviour and experience that can be categorized as "schizophrenia". The question, however, is how this pattern of behaviour and experience has developed in the diagnosed individual. We know quite a few people who, when they first heard voices, were not able to cope with their voices and developed a range of secondary reactions that mimic the whole range of schizophrenic behaviour and therefore were diagnosed as such. But when they started to listen to their voices and recognise their problems and were able to learn to cope with their problems they were also able to cope with their voices and the full range of reactions diminished or vanished.

Help

Therefore everyone who hears voices and is troubled by them, should be given the opportunity to assess their relationship with the voices. Their life experiences should be assessed for the underlying reasons for hearing voices, and this should be before they become diagnosed and are treated for an illness instead of being helped with their problems. The negative attitude of our society and our psychiatric services towards hearing voices and schizophrenia should be scrutinized. As long as that is not the case the Hearing Voices movement offers a unique opportunity for voice hearers to scrutinize their own victim status and help each other to overcome the negative attitude of the society the consequences of discrimination related to it.

This is changing and the proposal that you can work with 'voices' has increasing currency in the UK, in fact there is a danger that working with voices will become just another therapy. The cognitive behavioural therapists are particularly interested in assisting people to cope with their voices, but they do so without taking any position on the wider social meaning of the voice experience. They are happy to stay within the illness model. We have found that psychologists and nurses have been the most open professional groups and psychiatrists the most guarded.

If you are a mental health worker, family member or friend you could:

Start to accept the experience as a reality and ask what has happened in their life that could possibly relate to these mental health problems and to begin with the life issue or complaint that first led to the experiences.

If they are confused about that then you could go over their life history asking what has happened to them in terms of illnesses they may have had; a loss of a close person; a loved one; having had problems in relationships with others, such as friends, family, parents, brothers and sisters; losing a job or failing to find one; housing or financial problems. It is also important to consider problems with emotions like aggression, physical abuse or having been belittled or having been aggressive themselves; or with sexuality, such as problems with sexual identity or sexual abuse etc.

If they have experienced one or more of these events and describe the problem, you ask if it could have anything to do with their voices, their paranoia, their beliefs and personal convictions etc. You just have to be clear to yourself and to others that psychotic experiences do not fall from heaven, but are related to serious problems a person has suffered in real life.

Then you are on the way to detecting the person's problems and they might become less estranged from his/her self because of their psychotic experiences.

This takes time and you will meet also some resistance,

because people often do not like to be reminded of terrible experiences and might be ashamed of them.

Those people we know who are recovered all learned to express themselves, to give up shame and guilt after learning to manage their anxiety about their voices. They often wrote their stories down and then learned to talk about what has happened. Some people have even started to speak in public and discovered that they have had useful experiences, that they can share with others.

They started living their lives not their voices and visions

In the meantime you can try out some interventions to reduce your anxiety, as they are described in articles and publications about cognitive psychological interventions or you could read books like *Accepting Voices* or *Recovery an Alien Concept* and *Making Sense of Voices* and consider how you might use for yourself the possibilities that are described in these books (see further reading).

However, as long as there is a social taboo against voices, psychiatry will continue to maintain the role as custodian of this taboo. Because that is what psychiatry is set up for, to watch over societies interests in mental health affairs. In itself this is an important role when it is done correctly and effectively, unfortunately this is not the case as far as voice hearing is concerned.

There is hope though – the social taboo will change if by uniting people who hear voices, the movement becomes strong enough as a democratic force to realize that change, as has been the case with the gay movement.

Therefore it is a positive sign that there are not only national networks in 22 countries but that there is increasing international co-operation between the different countries within which the movement is developing.

The most important factor in the success of our approach is the importance placed on the personal engagement of the people involved. This means that everybody is considered an expert of their own experiences. We see each other first as people, secondly as equal partners and thirdly as all having different but mutually valuable expertise to offer. This can either be through direct experience of hearing voices or having worked with voice hearers (and/or wanting to).

Most recently we have seen significant developments in the USA and in September 2009 the first world hearing voices congress was held in Maastricht in the Netherlands with over 250 people present including many voice hearers from across the world. Since this work began over 20 years ago the movement has grown organically – I do not know what the next twenty years will bring but I fully expect the influence of the hearing voices movement to continue to grow and that there will be far reaching changes in the way people who voices are regarded by society.

You can can find out more about the Hearing Voices Movement by visiting our website at 'www.intervoiceonline.org' and join us in spreading positive and hopeful messages about the experience of hearing voices across the world.

GLOSSARY OF TERMS COMMONLY USED IN PSYCHIATRY AND PSYCHIATRIC RESEARCH

Auditory hallucinations (also see hearing voices): An hallucination is a sensory perception experienced in the absence of an external stimulus, as distinct from an illusion, which is regarded as a mis-perception of an external stimulus.

Clinical psychiatry: The branch of medicine that deals with the diagnosis, treatment, and prevention of mental and emotional disorders.

Cognitive psychological interventions: Cognitive and behavioural psychotherapies are a range of therapies based on concepts and principles derived from psychological models of human emotion and behaviour. They include a wide range of treatment approaches for emotional disorders, along a continuum from structured individual psychotherapy to self-help material.

Construct validity: refers to whether a scale measures the unobservable social construct that it purports to measure.

Core symptoms: The symptoms that lead to a diagnosis.

Delusion: commonly defined as a fixed false belief and is used in everyday language to describe a belief that is either false, fanciful or derived from deception. In psychiatry, the definition is necessarily more precise and implies that the belief is pathological (the result of an illness or illness process).

Diagnostic process: the process of identifying a disease by its signs, symptoms and results of various diagnostic procedures. The conclusion reached through that process is also called a diagnosis. The term "diagnostic criteria" designates the combination of symptoms which allows the doctor to ascertain the diagnosis of the respective disease.

Disease marker: associated with diseases that can be detected physically and used to determine whether an individual is at risk for developing a disease.

DSM: The Diagnostic and Statistical Manual of Mental Disorders (DSM-IV-TR), published by the American Psychiatric Association, is the handbook used most often in diagnosing mental disorders in the United States. The International Statistical Classification of Diseases and Related Health Problems (ICD) is a commonly-used alternative internationally. The DSM tends to be the more specific of the two. Both assume medical concepts and terms, and state that there are categorical disorders that can be diagnosed by set lists of criteria.

Effect size: is a measure of the strength of the relationship between two variables. In scientific experiments, it is often useful to know not only whether an experiment has a statistically significant effect, but also the size of any observed effects. In practical situations, effect sizes are helpful for making decisions. Effect size measures are the common currency of meta-analysis studies that summarise the findings from a specific area of research.

Hearing Voices: Perceptions of auditory experiences without an external stimulus and with a compelling sense of their reality.

Hypothetical construct: In scientific theory a hypothetical construct is an explanatory variable which is not directly observable.

Ideas of reference: Ideas of reference or delusions of reference involve a person having a belief or perception that things in the world are referring to them directly or have special personal significance. The two are clearly distinguished in psychological literature. People suffering from ideas of reference experience intrusive thoughts of this nature, but crucially, they realize that these ideas are not real. Those suffering from delusions of reference believe that these ideas are true.

Negative symptoms: Negative symptoms relate to those abilities or personality traits that are "lost" with schizophrenia. Negative symptoms usually occur first and may still be present during periods of remission as the disease progresses. Negative symptoms generally include: Apathy or lack of motivation; Self-neglect; Reduced or inappropriate emotion; Inability to experience pleasure; Loss of motivation to complete goals or tasks etc.

Neuroscience: Neuroscience is a scientific discipline that studies the structure, function, development, genetics, biochemistry, physiology, pharmacology, and pathology of the nervous system.

Psychiatric survivors: A number of people considered ill and needing treatment by specific psychiatrists or psychiatric doctrine in general do not perceive benefit from the services offered or forced upon them. Many respond with anger to the system which judges them to be ill because they consider there to be a value bias within it, that underlie the judgements made about them.

Psychopathology: The manifestation of behaviours and experiences which may be indicative of mental illness or psychological impairment. Any behaviour or experience which causes impairment, distress or disability, particularly if it is thought to arise from a functional breakdown in either the cognitive or neurocognitive systems in the brain, may be classified as psychopathology.

Psychosis: is a generic psychiatric term for a mental state in which thought and perception are severely impaired. Persons experiencing a psychotic episode may experience hallucinations, hold delusional beliefs (e.g., grandiose or paranoid delusions), demonstrate personality changes and exhibit disorganized thinking (see thought disorder). This is often accompanied by lack of insight into the unusual or bizarre nature of such behaviour, difficulties with social interaction and impairments in carrying out the activities of daily living. A psychotic episode is often described as involving a "loss of contact with reality".

Recovery: Recovery can be defined as a personal process of tackling the adverse impact of experiencing mental health problems, despite their continuing or long-term presence. Used in this sense, recovery does not mean "cure". Recovery is about people seeing themselves as capable of recovery rather than as passive recipients of professional interventions. The personal accounts of recovery suggest that much personal recovery happens without (or in some cases in spite of) professional help. Recovery involves personal development and change, including acceptance there are problems to face, a sense of involvement and control over one's life, the cultivation of hope and using the support from others, including collaborating in solution-focused work with informal carers and professional workers.

Schizophrenia: is said to be a type of mental illness. Schizophrenia causes problems with behaviour (the way people act), thinking, emotions, motivation and is linked to psychosis. People with schizophrenia are often thought to have 'lost touch with reality'.
The word schizophrenia comes from the Greek words σχίζω (schizo, break) and φρενός (frenos, mind) and means "shattered mind". Psychiatrist Emil Kraepelin was the first person to separate schizophrenia from other types of mental illness. He called it 'dementia praecox', and it was later renamed 'schizophrenia'.

Syndrome: In medicine, the term syndrome is the association of several clinically recognizable features, signs, symptoms, phenomena or characteristics which often occur together, so that the presence of one feature alerts the physician to the presence of the others. In recent decades the term has been used outside of medicine to refer to a combination of phenomena seen in association.

Trauma Induced Psychosis: Trauma and stress can cause psychosis. Major life-changing events such as the death of a family member or a natural disaster have been known to stimulate psychotic disorders.

Further Reading

Richard P Bentall, *Madness Explained: Psychosis and Human Nature*, (2004), Penguin, UK

Lisa Blackman: *Hearing Voices, Embodiment and Experience* (2001), Free Association Books, London; UK

Coleman R and M. Smith: *Victim to Victor: working with voices*, (1997) Working to Recovery, UK

Coleman R, *From Power to Partnership*, (1996) Handsell publications, UK

Coleman R, *Recovery – An Alien Concept*, (2006) 2nd Edition, P&P Press Limited, UK

Coleman R, *How to Set up and Run a Hearing Voices Group* (2009) DVD, Working to Recovery, UK

Julie Downs, (Ed), (2001) *Starting and Supporting Voices Groups: A Guide to setting up and running support groups for people who hear voices, see visions or experience tactile or other sensations*. Hearing Voices Network, Manchester, England

Downs J., (Ed), *Coping with Voices And Visions, A guide to helping people who Experience hearing voices, seeing visions, tactile or other Sensations*, (2001) Hearing Voices Network, Manchester, England

Adam James, *Raising Our Voices – an account of the Hearing Voices movement* (2001), Handsell Publishing, UK

J. Jaynes: *The origin of consciousness and the breakdown of the bicameral mind,* (1976) Houghton Mifflin, Boston

Leudar I and Thomas P: *Voices of Reason, Voices of Insanity – Studies of Verbal Hallucinations* (2000) published by Routledge/Psychological Press.

Romme M and Escher S: (Eds.), *Accepting Voices* (1993, second edition 1998), 258 pages, Mind Publications, London, UK.

Romme M, Honig A, Noorthorn EO & Escher S (1992): *Coping with hearing voices: an emancipatory approach.* British Journal of Psychiatry: July; 161:99-103

Romme M and Escher S (eds): *Understanding voices: coping with auditory hallucinations and confusing realities.* First published by Rijksuniversitiet Maastricht, Limburg, Holland (1996) and English edition, WTR Publications

Romme M and Escher S: *Making Sense of Voices – A guide for professionals who work with voice hearers,* (2000) Mind Publications, UK

Daniel B. Smith, *Muses, Madmen, and Prophets: Hearing Voices and the Borders of Sanity,* (2008) Penguin, USA

Philip Thomas, *The Dialectics of Schizophrenia* (1997) Free Association Books, UK

Watkins J, *Healing Schizophrenia: Using Medication Wisely* (2006) Michelle Anderson Publishing, Australia

Watkins J, *Hearing Voices – A Common Human Experience:*,(2008) Michelle Anderson Publishing, Australia